SOCIAL WO
PSYCHIATF
and the LAW

Norman N. Pringle
Senior Social Worker, Friern Hospital

Paul J. Thompson
Team Leader, Friern Hospital

WILLIAM HEINEMANN MEDICAL BOOKS
London

First published in 1986 by William Heinemann Medical Books Ltd,
23 Bedford Square, London WC1B 3HH

ISBN: 0–433–26320–2

Photoset by Wilmaset, Birkenhead, Wirral and
printed in Great Britain by Biddles Ltd, Guildford

Contents

Acknowledgements

In writing this acknowledgement, we are conscious of those too numerous to mention whose influence upon us enabled us to contemplate and bring to completion a work of this kind: our parents, our friends, our teachers.

In the preparation of the text, we would like to thank all our colleagues both at Friern Hospital and elsewhere for their help and advice at every stage of its development. For their assistance in individual aspects of the work we thank: Professor A. Wakeling, Dr N. Graham, Dr M. Conran, Dr P. T. D'Orban, Carl Ferguson, Lionel Tucker, Nurunnessa Choudhury, Dimitricus Skavalonous, Dr K. Loucas and Mary Barker. Any subsequent errors or omissions remain ours, not theirs.

Grateful thanks to Sue Holland for permission to reproduce Fig. 9.1 and text from her 1984 lecture in Chapter 9.

Especial thanks to our secretaries, Noreen, Marcia and Greta, and also Friern Hospital's Library Staff, Mrs E. Eames and Jenny Griffiths, for all their work.

We must thank Iris Nutting for her generous help at the inception of our work together.

For his patience, help, and encouragement, we thank Dr Richard Barling of William Heinemann Medical Books.

Introduction

The Mental Health Act 1959, which set the seal on mental health thinking for over twenty years has now been replaced by The Mental Health Act 1983. This provided the opportunity for a transformation in our thought and work. It introduced the concept of the Approved Social Worker. It clearly put the emphasis on community care; the onus on patient's rights. This has important implications for everyone working with the mentally ill and particularly social workers, psychiatric nurses and those providing community care.

This book is intended for all workers concerned with the field of mental health. It is intended as a contribution to the increase in awareness and skills now recognised as necessary for the development of services for the mentally ill. We have brought together social work, psychiatric services and mental health legislation in order to discuss these both individually and in their relation to one another. We have endeavoured to make this a practical handbook for approved social workers to help them fulfil their role under the 1983 Act.

The history of mental health provision reflects the changing social attitudes towards the mentally ill. In the eighteenth century when poor law officers were authorised to detain paupers in madhouses under the 1712 and 1744 Vagrancy Acts, the main aim was to control and contain and to keep the mentally ill out of sight of the rest of the population. The 1983 Mental Health Act moves away from the mental welfare officer towards the approved social worker who is legally required to play a major role in deciding who should be detained in hospital and has the responsibility to look at alternatives and involve families. There is also a duty on approved social workers to protect the legal rights of the patient and his relatives.

The reorganisation of the local authority social services, which took place in 1971, brought major changes and it has been argued that some of the expertise on mental health was lost as social services departments strove to meet the increasing pressures and demands made upon them. At the same time the concept of mental welfare officers simply acting as substitutes for relatives and following the statutory procedures at the request of the general practitioner or psychiatrist was increasingly questioned. Not infrequently there was confusion, misunderstanding and uncertainty which gave rise to inter-disciplinary disagreement, especially between family doctors and social workers. More generally, there was concern to distinguish between the need for medical assessment of the potential patient's condition, the need for independent assessment of the social conditions influencing behaviour and the need to protect civil liberties.

Mental health is about people in situations. Social workers have always tried to look at a situation from a number of perspectives, and the 1983 Mental Health Act makes this mandatory in law. Let us consider the case of a young mother with two small children, who has an acute onset of a psychotic breakdown. She is filled with the overwhelming belief that the devil is present and is coming to destroy her two children because they are too good to stay with her. She hears the devil's voice prompting her to kill the children and the whole dilemma comes to a head when she prepares a sacrificial meal containing poison. An anxious health visitor calls the general practitioner who decides that she is mentally ill and needs to go to hospital. He calls in the social worker.

In such an emergency the social worker is called on to keep in mind a number of points of view, some of which seem to conflict with each other. For example:

1. What is the medical recommendation?
2. Is this lady a danger to herself or to others?
3. Is she agreeable to go into hospital, either as an in-patient or as a day patient?
4. What are the social factors which are likely to have precipitated the crisis?
5. Is hospital the most appropriate form of help?
6. What are the statutory and legal requirements to enforce any course of action?
7. What are the client's rights at assessment?

The approved social worker has to consider all these factors and more before deciding whether to apply for the client to be admitted to hospital and has to take responsibility for that decision.

Let us imagine that our imaginary client, at the time of the crisis, refuses to talk to the social worker and remains absolutely mute. However, her husband can respond to counselling and he suggests that the children could be cared for by his mother and, in fact, would certainly have to be if his wife goes into hospital. In the absence of the children, has the immediate criteria for her being compulsorily admitted any validity?

These are some of the issues facing social workers in mental health crises. These issues themselves can also get inside us as social workers, often making us react in ways which we may not understand.

We hope that this contribution will go some way towards clarifying our tasks, responsibilities and limitations as social workers so that, at the very least, we may sometimes be able to 'keep our feet on the ground' when all about us are losing their heads and perhaps blaming it on us!

A note on language

For ease of reading we have consistently used the male pronoun throughout the text.

Preface

The Mental Health Act 1959 was brought into operation at the end of 1960. It covered all forms of mental disorder and replaced the Lunacy Acts of 1880 and 1881, the Mental Treatment Act 1930 (in respect of mental illness) and the Mental Deficiency Act 1913–38 (in respect of what is now called mental sub-normality and severe sub-normality). In one complete Act it replaced the former patchwork of legislation.

The 1959 Act came into being as the direct result of the report of the Royal Commission on the law relating to mental illness and mental deficiency published in 1957. Apart from those parts which related to the making of special financial provisions to help local authorities in carrying out their duties under the Act, the report was accepted virtually in its entirety. The objects of the Act were to bring the law into line with the climate of public opinion and modern psychiatric thought and practice. The intention was to change the whole atmosphere of the law being mainly concerned with custodial care, largely long term in hospital, to one of positive treatment, as far as practical within the community, and where this is not possible, leading to an early return of the patient to the community. The Act introduced the requirement for social workers dealing with assessments for compulsory admission to be trained and approved as 'competent'.

The 1983 Mental Health Act sets out to clarify the responsibilities of social workers approved for statutory duties. Clause 16 of the amendment to the Act states as follows:

'Before making an application for the admission of a patient to hospital, the authorised Social Worker shall interview the patient and satisfy himself that the detention in a hospital is in all the circumstances of the case, the most appropriate way of providing the care and medical treatment of which the patient stands in need.'

That is to say that the approved social workers must see for themselves what the prospective patient is like, must assess the social circumstances and make a judgement of the best course of action in the light of the medical opinion about the client's condition and all other circumstances. This degree of responsibility, which includes the power to compel a person to go into hospital, calls for a high level of expertise from social workers; it creates powerful and often unacknowledged demands on our own emotional and intellectual reserves.

Part I

Social work practice and psychiatry

Chapter 1

Psychiatric Illness: Neuroses, Psychoses

Most of us from time to time experience emotional distress and, indeed, we may regard this as normal. The degree of emotional suffering that many of our clients experience can be related to external causes in their lives. Here we begin by looking at the major patterns of distress as they are classified in terms of psychiatric illness. We will deal first with the milder forms of mental disorder: the psychoneurotic conditions, in which the sufferer may experience considerable distress, and where his ability to manage is incapacitated. We will then go on to look at the psychotic conditions, where the capacity to manage is much more severely impaired.

NEUROSES

The neuroses are the milder psychiatric disorders. Reality is less distorted than in the psychoses and insight is retained. The four main groups of neurosis are:

1. Anxiety states.
2. Obsessional compulsive disorders.
3. Hysteria.
4. Reactive or neurotic depression.

ANXIETY STATES

Anxiety is a normal enough state for most of us to understand. Indeed the anxiety states are probably the commonest of all psychiatric disorders and make up a large proportion of the complaints which bring patients to consult their GPs and clients to consult social workers.

A person suffering from anxiety neurosis is likely to complain of a number of symptoms, ranging from mild apprehension to feelings of acute panic. Many describe an almost constant state of anxiety, where there are physical sensations of choking, or fears of going out alone or into crowded places like restaurants. A feeling of 'free floating' anxiety may be felt for no apparent reason. Such fears can sometimes make it impossible for a person to function. In other cases, physical symptoms of headaches, palpitations and frequency of urination may be present. If patients believe that they have a diseased organ, for which there is no medical evidence, this is called hypochondriasis. Behind many complaints of headaches and lack of sleep brought to GPs, there is an underlying anxiety state. It should be stressed that worry is normal. It motivates us to take action and to make decisions, but worry which is overwhelming and undefined can inhibit and seriously incapacitate the sufferer.

Treatment

Clinically, most neurotic anxiety is seen and dealt with by the GP rather than by the psychiatrist. Treatment can take the form of reassurance and support for minor complaints, going on to out-patient psychotherapy or medication for more serious complaints, such as the apparently chronically anxious patient. The specific medication is usually of benzodiazepine drugs, including Valium and Librium. Psychotherapy can be used to enable patients to gain insight into underlying conflicts which may be sustaining these symptoms.

Clearly, social workers can play an important role in both recognising neurotic anxiety and referring sufferers to their GPs for assessment. In addition, social workers will be able to assess any social or economic stresses which may be contributing to their client's feelings of anxiety, and help them deal with these problems.

OBSESSIONAL COMPULSIVE DISORDERS

Most of us will be familiar with the experience of having a tune that goes around and around in our head, or a senseless idea which occurs repeatedly. With the obsessive patient such experiences are felt to a crippling degree. These obsessions often take the form of thoughts which are intrusive and keep occurring in the patient's mind against his will. These thoughts can often be of a violent or obscene nature or contain fears of contamination.

Compulsions occur as a response to these thoughts. They are irresistible urges to perform an act or a protective ritual in an attempt to ward off the anxiety that such thoughts generate. Such patients fear that if they do not carry out these rituals they will face retribution, such as eternal damnation. The most common compulsive acts are checking and hand washing. The sufferer can become preoccupied for hours, checking and rechecking to see whether he has turned off a gas tap. This can be extended to checking doors and windows until most of his day is taken up with such activity. Handwashing is a ritual which is often related to fear of contamination. The patient usually has a special way of washing, and this can be repeated up to 40 times a day until the intense anxiety lessens. The number of times the patient needs to perform this ritual can often achieve a magical significance.

The type of person most prone to this disorder is likely to have been described as 'a very worthy citizen' as he is neat, tidy and orderly. However, such individuals tend to be too rigid and carry their desire for orderliness too far. Their behaviour can put considerable strain on relatives. To try to prevent a patient from carrying out rituals can only increase his anxiety, which leads in turn to an increase in his compulsive behaviour. People who seem to be most vulnerable to developing such disorders are those who are obsessive. The World Health Organisation International Classification of Diseases calls this type of personality disorder 'anankastic' and defines it thus:

> 'Personality disorder characterised by feelings of personal insecurity, doubt and incompleteness leading to excessive conscientiousness, checking, stubborness and caution. There may be insistent and unwelcome thoughts or impulses which do not attain the severity of an obsessional neurosis. There is perfectionism and meticulous accuracy and a need to check repeatedly in an attempt to ensure this. Rigidity and excessive doubt may be conspicuous.'

Clearly not all such individuals who show these traits become ill.

Treatment
Medication: tranquillisers do help to ease some of the intense distress provoked by the compulsive feeling associated with these disorders. They do little, however, to alter the underlying causes of the disorder. Psychosurgery is sometimes prescribed for patients who have had this illness for a long period and for the sufferer who has such severe symptoms that it cripples his ability to live life in any meaningful or satisfactory way.

In less severe cases, behaviour therapy might be considered. In cases where there is an obsessional compulsive component, which is diffused and generalised rather than converted into a specific symptom, psychotherapy may be considered. An example would be a patient with the feeling that everything must be checked two or three times, but then it is safe, as contrasted with a patient who cannot actually move away from a door for several hours because he is not sure, but must check repeatedly, that it is locked.

HYSTERIA

Hysteria is a term which is now used in general parlance to describe someone who is 'out of control', or it is sometimes used, inaccurately, as a term of abuse. The word comes from the Greek and means 'womb'. Many of the symptoms of hysteria are found more commonly in women; these are unconsciously motivated and can often mimic physical illness. It is therefore crucial that a thorough medical examination is carried out to eliminate any physical basis for the symptoms.

The World Health Organisation definition might help us to understand some of the basic personality characteristics of this disorder:

> 'Personality disorder characterised by shallow, labile affectivity, dependence on others, craving for appreciation and attention, suggestibility and theatricality. There is often sexual immaturity, e.g. frigidity and other over-responsiveness to stimuli. Under stress hysterical symptoms (neuroses) may develop.'

Conversion hysteria

A hysterical conversion symptom usually involves the sensory or motor systems of the body. It has no neurological basis but is in response to some unconscious psychological conflict and often provides some 'gain' for the sufferer.

These gains can be divided into:

1. Primary gain: first described by Freud; this gives relief from some intolerable intra-psychic conflict.
2. Secondary gain: demanding help or allowing the patient to escape from some stressful situation. Such hysterical symptoms are manifold; for example, they can include paralysis, tremor, deafness, blindness and fits.

Hysterical dissociation

This process is similar to hysterical conversion (i.e. conflict followed by repression followed by symptom formation). The conversion symptom is sensory/motor while hysterical dissociation involves narrowing the field of consciousness with selective amnesia (loss of memory).

Fugue (wandering states)

The patient may lead a double existence for a while, adopting an alternative identity (for example, in its more extreme form Dr Jekyll and Mr Hyde). The person may suddenly find himself in London away from his familiar home in Newcastle. He cannot remember why or how he arrived. In other words, the process is unconscious, and can be seen as a flight from a painful and stressful situation which the individual wants to escape. Such patients often recall the events after a period of a few weeks with the aid of abreactive procedures.

Munchausen's syndrome

This is a strange dissociative state where the person simulates signs and symptoms of an organic disease. The histories that such individuals present are often plausible enough to warrant extensive investigation and, in some cases, surgery. Such patients often travel from one hospital to another, where they have tests repeated over and over again. The tragedy is that their real emotional needs often go unmet and they tend to continue their pattern of behaviour.

Hysteria and malingering

It is important to try to distinguish between hysteria and malingering. The hysterical conversion symptoms and dissociation have an *unconscious* conflict as a cause of their behaviour. The malingerer is *consciously* aware of his abnormal behaviour.

Treatment

The treatment of hysteria has two main approaches. Where the disability has been caused by a traumatic experience in the individual's life, abreaction may be indicated. In this approach, the patient is given drugs or hypnosis to help him recall and relive the trauma. Dramatic improvements can sometimes occur when the patient re-experiences, what are often, painful events.

In more entrenched conditions where the hysterical symptoms are a part of a more disturbed personality structure, a long-term approach such as psychotherapy may be indicated. This will help the patient to gain insight into the unconscious factors which are creating his difficulties. A working through towards a better adjustment can then be achieved.

Behaviour therapy is also a useful approach. Here the focus would be on how the patient's use of 'secondary gain' is helping to sustain his illness: that is, what ends are being satisfied by his being ill.

The social worker's role is important in establishing and understanding the patient's current life stresses so that these may be addressed in the whole treatment programme. It is often in alleviating the social stresses that the client may gain greater control of his life.

REACTIVE OR NEUROTIC DEPRESSION

Neurotic depression is usually felt in response to a distressing experience of some kind. It does not include as its characteristics delusions or hallucinations. There is often some preoccupation with a psychic trauma which precedes the illness. Examples of this could be loss of a person, pet, limb, or a function (e.g. sudden blindness); physical illness—past or impending; life changes such as retirement. Anxiety is also frequently present and mixed states of anxiety and depression are included in the psychiatric definition.

It is important to distinguish between neurotic depression and psychotic depression. This is done on the basis of degree of depression, and also on the presence or absence of other neurotic and psychotic characteristics, e.g. delusions and nihilistic beliefs, and upon the degree of disturbance of the patient's behaviour.

The clinical classification of a neurotic depression should not be confused with general or specific feelings of unhappiness, which many people experience. This unhappiness can arise for many reasons and take many forms. Neurotic depression is a specific clinical description of a mental state.

Treatment
Psychoanalytic findings highlight the sense of guilt which is nearly always present in the depressed person—sometimes obviously, but not always so! When working with neurotically depressed people, it can be a great help to them to get in touch with this sense of guilt. Reassurance cannot dispel it, but listening to patients talk about why they feel guilty can help them come to a more rational sense of self.

Medication can alleviate some of the worst feelings of a neurotic depression, and can act as a holding mechanism until other therapeutic forces can take effect. Counselling and psychotherapy are two key treatments of a neurotic depression. When the distressing factors are still present—for example housing or financial worries—it is obviously of importance to try to alleviate these difficulties.

Social work with the depressed patient

Depression has become an umbrella term to describe those painful emotional states associated with loss, stressful circumstances such as illness, unemployment, handicap and disturbed relationships. With some clients the cause of depression may not be so clear, for example many clients experience depression as an almost permanent feature of their personality and it is increased at times of stress. Yet with others depression seems to appear from out of the blue and has no apparent external cause.

Depression is a very variable condition and can range from feelings of profound sadness to severe states where the patient is stuporised, mute and inaccessible. Trigger factors like loss and disappointment can precipitate depressive reactions and, even in the most severe states, painful life events can be traced to three months prior to the onset of the episode.

Most cases of clinical depression are treated by the GP or a psychiatrist on an out-patient basis with a combination of antidepressant medication and supportive psychotherapy. In the more severe states electro-convulsive therapy (ECT) may be indicated.

What is depression?

Depression is a complex emotional state involving an interplay of feelings such as fear and rage which seem to turn themselves against each other producing a painful depressed mood. In addition, the person often experiences a slowing down of mental and physical processes. This is often accompanied by an overriding feeling of helplessness and inability to change his situation. In the more extreme cases the depressed person may believe that he deserves to suffer through a sense of guilt and wickedness. Because of the nature of the disorder he may feel unworthy and not turn for help but continue to suffer in silence. Alternatively the depressed person may present more subtle symptoms like aches and pains and the underlying depression may go unrecognised even by the skilled professional.

Depression is clearly not a simple condition but involves many factors, for instance, the basic personality of the individual to bear and manage feelings of loss; intra-psychic conflict; external stresses; and in the more severe conditions biochemical factors may play a part.

The psycho-social hurdle

Whatever the cause of depression the patient cannot recover totally in a medical vacuum. Medical treatment may enable many cases to feel better and give them greater access to their energy and drives. The social worker will need to help the patient capitalise on this and help him over the psycho-social hurdle into his wider world. It is not uncommon to discover that the depressed patient has few friends. His low self-esteem prevents him, in many cases, from forming and sustaining lasting relationships. As a general rule the fewer the social and inter-personal resources the patient has, the less responsive he will be to any kind of treatment and this, in turn, will prolong his recovery.

Casework may need to focus on helping the patient gain a firmer grasp of the internal and external reasons for his depression. This will enable him to work with the processes that make handling depression difficult. Ideally this process should start alongside the medical approach and continue until the patient feels well enough to cope alone.

The casework relationship

Clearly the external causes for the patient's depression must be addressed and resolved as the primary task. However, we must go further. The patient invariably feels bad about himself. What's more, he feels others cannot tolerate him either and this deep attitude often militates against understanding and help. It is through the casework relationship that the patient can begin to feel accepted and helped with what he feels is unbearable within himself. Through this the patient will gradually begin to experience the social worker as someone who can accept and bear the patient's depression. We must bear some of the patient's psychic pain, so as to enable the patient to do so. This is the essential key to achieving this kind of change, for it is not until the patient is convinced that the feelings of his 'badness' can be borne that he can begin to integrate them into his whole personality without them overwhelming him.

The social worker may well meet a deep self-defeating attitude within the patient which can easily be turned against social workers or those who try to help him. The social worker will need to help him and work with this aspect of the patient's personality if he is to change. Through this process of working through these feelings the patient will begin to realise that his negative side is not all powerful. He will see his anger, resentment and other deep negative parts for what they are—aspects of himself—and begin to integrate them alongside his more positive feelings.

ANOREXIA NERVOSA

This disorder can arise at any age, but tends to occur mainly in adolescent girls soon after puberty: this is designated primary anorexia nervosa.

When it occurs in women aged 20 and over it is termed secondary anorexia nervosa. The younger age group tends far to outnumber the older age group. It rarely occurs in males. Anorexia nervosa appears to be on the increase; it is now commonly known as 'slimmers' illness'.

The familiar pattern of the anorexic patient is that she will gradually cut out fattening food, first bread and potatoes, then begin to refuse milk and sugar in drinks. At first, those around may believe that the person has a food fad, or is on a special diet. However, the illness then commonly develops into a self-starvation campaign, where if it continues untreated, death from starvation can occur. In many severe cases there is an accompanying risk of infection: being undernourished, the body lacks resistance and may not be able to cope with even mild illnesses. The mortality rate amongst anorexia sufferers can be as high as 10% if the anorexia goes untreated.

During the course of the illness, the patient becomes amenorrhoeal (i.e. ceases to menstruate) and severely emaciated. Because of the risks already mentioned, it will generally be necessary to admit the anorexia sufferer to hospital where she can be nursed under close supervision to ensure that the prescribed therapeutic diet is actually taken. Patients with anorexia can be extremely deceitful about their food intake, going to great lengths to hide the food and pretend that they have eaten it. Many patients take large doses of appetite suppressants, for they mistakenly believe that this will hasten the slimming process.

The duration of anorexia nervosa can be from two to seven years; in some cases it can become chronic, or frequently recurring. Even after regaining weight, menstruation may not recommence for several months.

Treatment

Treatment of such patients can be difficult. Two broad approaches are used. One consists of using behaviour therapy—operant conditioning—where the patient receives privileges as progress is made over the preplanned treatment programme. These may include receiving visits or being allowed to make telephone calls. This approach may also include medication to aid appetite and tranquillise the patient.

In the second main treatment approach, chlorpromazine is given in large doses to tranquillise the patient, prevent vomiting, and stimulate appetite. As the patient begins to put on weight, and the symptomatic improvement is made, psychotherapy may be introduced to explore and treat the underlying causes of the disorder. In many cases family therapy is useful, for much of the disturbance associated with this disorder can be traced back to factors within the family as a group.

Food may have a profound symbolic importance within the family, for example, and the rejection of food can therefore be a key way of rejecting an unwanted family. Family therapy can make contact with these unacknowledged aspects of family functioning, and alleviate the causes which perpetuate the disorder.

Medical opinion is divided about the causes of the disorder of anorexia. This can be reflected in the different treatment approaches used. For example, anorexia can be seen as being a psychological regression to childhood, and a consequent denial of developing womanhood.

BULIMIA NERVOSA

This is a disorder related to anorexia nervosa, both in terms of client group and symptomatology. Bulimia is characterised by eating, followed by vomiting. Eating is often undertaken in large amounts or 'binges'; vomiting often carried out in secret. Thus this can be quite a difficult disorder to detect. Bulimia nervosa is a severe neurotic disorder. Body weight can fluctuate dramatically as in anorexia.

Treatment
Where there is sufficient motivation, individual or group psychotherapy can help alleviate this condition. One method of group psychotherapy can be for a group of bulimic sufferers to meet regularly (i.e. weekly) keeping records of their eating and vomiting habits in the intervening period. This can help induce some control and understanding into their actions.

CAUSES OF NEUROSIS

It is probably fair to say that the causes of neurosis and particular neurotic conditions are difficult to determine with any degree of certainty. In order to understand a neurosis, the whole person, together with his background and upbringing, needs to be considered and taken into account. In particular, anxiety states may be triggered off by life events and social conditions.

Psychoanalysis has emphasised the unconscious conflicts which can lead to neurotic symptoms. For instance, an obsessional compulsive patient might have an unconscious sense of destructiveness. The consequent feeling of guilt which this generates leads him to feel that it is only by his obsessive actions that he can prevent something very precious — perhaps the world or himself, he does not really know— from being destroyed.

PSYCHOSES

The psychoses are the most severe forms of mental disorders. These include the schizophrenias, manic depression and the organic psychoses. The personalities of such individuals are often fundamentally disturbed, and this can often lead to very disorganised and disruptive behaviour. In the case of the schizophrenic, for example, the patient may hear voices (auditory hallucinations) and believe himself to be the subject of some fantastic scheme (delusions).

These symptoms can often create a nightmare world in the sufferer where distortions of reality become so marked he is unable to distinguish between what is real in his inner and outer world and what is delusional. This is usually referred to as a lack of insight. Because the psychotic process confuses and distorts it can often lead to great confusion and bewilderment to the patient and all those around him.

Psychoses

Functional   Organic

Affective   Schizophrenia   Acute delirium   Chronic
disorders   states   (senile dementia)

Fig. 1.1   Types of psychotic illness.

Broadly speaking, the psychoses can be divided into those known as *functional psychoses*, which are normally of unknown aetiology, and *organic psychoses*, in which there is evidence of transient or permanent brain damage. The functional psychoses are subdivided into the *affective disorders* in which the primary disturbance is of mood or affect, and *schizophrenia* in which disorders of thinking, emotion and behaviour occur. This scheme is illustrated in Fig. 1.1. We will look at the organic psychoses in more detail in Chapter 3.

FUNCTIONAL PSYCHOSES: AFFECTIVE DISORDERS

The main affective disorders are depression and mania. They can occur alone (unipolar) or they can alternate, forming the manic depressive cycle (bipolar). The bipolar disorder is usually recurring, often with long periods of remission where the patient lives a normal life. The commonest disorder of mood in this group is depression. It is the most severe type of depression and it is called endogenous (psychotic) depression. The term means 'to arise from within the person'. However, such depression can be triggered off by life events. These can sometimes be traced to events in the patient's life three months before the onset of the episode.

We will now trace the development of a depressive illness.

PSYCHOTIC DEPRESSION

Here, the patient is profoundly depressed. If untreated the illness follows a characteristic course where the depression and the other presenting symptoms progress over a period of weeks until the maximum severity of the illness is reached. It may then remain for some time until a gradual improvement occurs. The durations of these episodes are variable, but can last from a few weeks to several months. Treatment in the form of antidepressant medication or ECT dramatically shorten such episodes. In about 50% of cases, there is no further episode but in the remainder, there may be recurrences, and these may be at critical times, i.e. childbirth, or during other critical life events.

The depressed patient usually feels at his worst first thing in the morning when characteristically he awakes early and it is not until the day proceeds that he begins to feel a bit better. His appetite is usually affected, he eats little and soon begins to lose weight. The patient's physical and mental activity is slowed down by a process known as retardation. This will be reflected in a marked slowness of his thoughts, speech and movements of his body. On a mental level he will find it difficult to concentrate, think and make decisions. A marked loss of drive is present. He may withdraw from social contacts and his usual interests. He may become mute and inaccessible. There may also be increased anxiety which may manifest itself in agitation or restless behaviour.

In severe cases delusions occur. These can be related to unworthiness, moral worth, health, financial position or social relationships. These delusions can develop into delusions of a nihilistic nature where the patient may believe he is dead or that his insides are rotting away with cancer. The patient may be quite wealthy but believe himself to be poor or bankrupt. By far the commonest delusions are those related to ill health or hypochondria.

Suicide must always be regarded as a high risk. The patient may believe that life is not worth living and kill himself. In very rare and extreme cases, he may murder his wife and family then kill himself.

Treatment

Because of the great risk of suicide such patients will need to be admitted to hospital, if necessary on a compulsory order. Many psychiatrists see ECT as the first treatment of choice in such disorders. Antidepressant medication takes a few weeks before it becomes effective. Certainly the evidence suggests that this is the one condition which improves dramatically after ECT and because of the urgent need to intervene it will often be used first, perhaps alongside a course of antidepressant medication. Most psychiatrists now use lithium carbonate after the severe depression has lifted, both as a treatment and more long term as a preventive measure.

MANIA OR HYPOMANIA

Mania or hypomania is more commonly seen as a bipolar affective disorder. That is to say, the manic phase of the manic depressive cycle; where manic states alternate with severe depressive episodes. Between these states there are often long periods of remission in which the patient is well and carries out a normal life. Hypomania is a much less common disorder than depression.

In contrast to the depressive phase, the manic patient is elated, carefree and apparently unconcerned. The degree of the disorder is variable, for example, he may at first just seem to be in a bouncy optimistic mood and the illness may progress considerably before relatives realise there is something wrong. His mood may become euphoric, expansive and an infectious sense of gaiety takes over. There is considerable pressure of speech and flight of ideas where the patient swiftly passes from one topic to the next. He may then begin to express extraordinary ideas of his power and importance and these can develop into grandiose delusions. It is not uncommon for such patients to become involved in senseless schemes which can turn out to be financially and socially disastrous to the patient and his family.

At one level the manic patient can often be amusing and attractive and draw adherents. However, his overwhelming behaviour soon becomes exhausting and exasperating to relatives, friends and colleagues. As his behaviour becomes more out of control and disinhibited this can lead to embarrassing situations and, if this is allowed to continue, the person's relationships and reputation may be put in peril. If he feels obstacles are being put in his way he will suddenly become irritable and angry; for beneath his overactivity he is vulnerable and sensitive to criticism and will respond to feeling thwarted with verbal abuse. Although physical aggression is uncommon, manic patients can express considerable verbal hostility.

Treatment

Because the patient's behaviour is usually out of control he is likely to be at risk in several areas. On a physical level he may not find time to eat or sleep and his constant activity may produce exhaustion. On a financial and social level, his excessive spending may lead to financial difficulties where his socially disturbed behaviour may ruin his reputation amongst his family, friends and colleagues at work. For example, it is not uncommon for manic patients to make major life decisions when they are ill. They may change their religion, partner or job which they may later bitterly regret. It is important to get hypomanic excitement under rapid control before it escalates into mania or plunges into depression.

In order to carry out the necessary treatment it will nearly always be necessary for the patient to be admitted to hospital. Drug therapy needs to be introduced right away to help reduce the psycho motor activity. Chlopromazine and Haliperidol are given in appropriate doses. Once the episode of mania is under control the psychiatrist may decide to introduce lithium carbonate to continue to stabilise the mood. Lithium carbonate has enabled considerable progress to be made in the treatment and prevention of those who suffer from recurrent attacks of mania and depression.

Social work with the hypomanic patient

The normal personality of the hypomanic patient tends to swing between extreme moods: elation to depression; exuberance to withdrawal. In a clinical sense, he is said to be cyclothymic. It may be some time before it is realised by others that his behaviour has gone beyond the bounds of what is rational and tolerable. By this time much damage may have occurred before professional help is sought. Although many people function at a high energy level and are often creative and successful, it is only when such behaviour oversteps the mark and the patient becomes out of control and puts himself and others at risk that intervention is necessary.

Most patients who reach this level of their illness are impulsive, reckless and lacking any insight into their behaviour and need for help. Because of this it may not be possible to gain their cooperation and help. They may not see themselves as ill; indeed they may feel on top of the world. In the most severe cases they will need to be admitted to hospital, if necessary on a compulsory basis, to avoid further harm to themselves and others.

Assessment

Here are some of the factors which the approved social worker will need to consider and balance when making an assessment to decide the most appropriate course of action to help the patient and his family. Because of the behaviour already described, the patient is likely to be at risk in several areas.

1. On a physical level he may feel too busy to eat, drink or sleep, and this constant activity may put him at great risk through physical exhaustion and malnutrition.

2. Hypomania, if not checked, is in danger of escalating into mania or plunging into depression.

3. On a social and financial level his extravagant and disinhibited behaviour may lead to ruin. For example, it is not uncommon for such patients to enter into senseless financial schemes or run up considerable debts through hire purchase arrangements which can dissipate life savings or spend money which they do not have through cheques and credit cards. Socially uninhibited behaviour can create social damage to himself, family, friends and colleagues and if it is allowed to go unchecked can destroy his career and relationships. When the patient is well he will bitterly regret this and might find it difficult to undo the harm he has done.

4. If thwarted in their extravagant demands hypomanic patients can become angry and, if pressed, violent. This can create additional stresses and difficulties when family and friends want to limit the patient's activities, and is one reason why compulsory admission may be helpful.

5. Hypomanic patients generally don't feel ill. If asked how they are, they will often reply, 'on top of the World', or 'never felt better'. This can be deceptive unless the assessment takes account of other factors such as the testimony of family and friends, the patient's usual behaviour and their physical appearance (the hypomanic patient may appear slightly dishevelled, tired looking, may wear extraordinary clothing and will probably find it very difficult to sit still for long).

The aftermath

The emotional and social consequences of a hypomanic attack can leave everyone around feeling devastated. As the patient emerges from the episode and realises what damage he has done he may become depressed and remorseful. This can lead to profound depression and set up a different set of problems. Because his behaviour is often distressing to those around him he is likely to be the target of their wrath. Often the family routine has been upset, they may have been kept awake at night for long periods and have had to put up with all sorts of abuse and demands, which may well leave them feeling resentful and angry. The toll on such families can be heavy and they may well need casework help to deal with the emotional havoc that such episodes create. In some cases the disruption may have been so great for the spouse that she may feel no longer able to cope with the relationship. This is especially so where she has already experienced previous episodes of the illness and begins to fear further ones.

Casework plans need to include a medical opinion so that work can be done around the actual diagnosis and prognosis of the disorder, for this may be central to the issues which will be raised in the casework relationship. Hypomania can be variable and generally can be controlled with medication such as lithium carbonate and other drugs. This, of course, requires the cooperation of the patient and perhaps the family to ensure it is taken regularly. The family may also need help to spot the first signs of the disorder so that the patient can be referred for early medical help. Such signs as increased irritability, sleeplessness and a more expansive mood in a person, with a previous history of hypomania, may be heralding another episode. Often a patient in the early stages of illness will have insight and it is important to gain his cooperation whilst he is amenable. Left to his own devices the illness may progress and this insight is lost, making it extremely difficult to engage with the patient and gain his goodwill. If these early signs are dealt with quickly, the patient's behaviour may not reach the stage where violation of conventions and dangerous actions necessitate hospital admission. Although the emotional aspect of hypomania is important, the client and his family will need practical help to deal with the consequences of his irresponsible behaviour. For example, it may be possible to arrange with the doctor in charge of his case for a medical certificate so that financial contracts entered into, while the patient was ill, can be terminated. It may also be possible for expensive articles that have been bought during the illness to be returned if the hospital can reassure the firms involved that the person was disturbed at the time they were purchased.

FUNCTIONAL PSYCHOSES: SCHIZOPHRENIA

Schizophrenia is the most severe of all the functional psychoses. The illness occurs more often in adolescence and in early adult life but it can present in middle and old age. The term 'schizophrenia' means 'splitting or fragmentation' of the mind and does not refer to the double 'Jekyll and Hyde' type of personality. It is perhaps best thought of as a group of related disorders which produces disorganisation of the personality. If the illness goes untreated there is a progressive disintegration often affecting judgement, emotions and behaviour. Delusions and auditory hallucinations are often present.

In Britain the mainstream of psychiatrists use the concepts of Kurt Schneider when diagnosing schizophrenia. He has identified a group of symptoms which he regards as 'first rank' in differentiating schizophrenia from other conditions. These are:

1. Thought disorders:
   (a) Thought insertion: the belief that thoughts are being inserted in one's mind from outside.
   (b) Thought withdrawal: the belief that thoughts are taken out of one's mind from outside.
   (c) Thought broadcasting: the belief that thoughts become known to others.
2. Auditory hallucinations: these are voices heard discussing one's thoughts or behaviour as they occur, like a running commentary. Hearing Voices: these are voices talking about the patient in the third person. Such voices are often abusive, ridiculing or derogatory.
3. Primary delusions: the patient may suddenly have an unshakeable belief that a particular set of events has special meaning to him and he will develop an elaborate delusional system.

In Schneider's view, if any person has one of these symptoms in the absence of organic or physical disturbance the diagnosis points to schizophrenia.

The incidence of schizophrenia is just under 1% of the population. This figure appears to be fairly even throughout the world. Schizophrenia often accounts for some 15% of admissions to mental hospitals. About 45% of the long stay population of mental hospitals are schizophrenics. The illness is more common in males than females and most cases occur before the age of 30.

The prognosis of schizophrenia is variable. For example, the speed of onset of the illness is significant. There seems to be a more favourable prognosis where the condition develops acutely, and the previous personality was fairly well integrated. With the more insidious onset, grown slowly out of a withdrawn schizoid personality, the prognosis is poorer. Up to about one third of patients do not recover, except from their acute symptoms; they may be left with severe mental disabilities. In all cases of schizophrenia prompt treatment is essential to avoid further deterioration.

The general signs and symptoms of schizophrenia

These can be grouped under four main disorders:

1. Thought.
2. Perception.
3. Emotion.
4. Behaviour.

Thought disorder

Many schizophrenia sufferers find it difficult to put their thoughts together in a comprehensible way. Their thinking often shows displacement or the use of associated thoughts for the correct ones. There can be a disorder in the flow of thoughts, when the patient will suddenly stop and then carry on a train of thought which may be totally unconnected with the first one. This is known as 'thought blocking'. Schneiderian first rank symptoms of thought insertion, thought withdrawal and thought broadcasting may also be present.

Disorders of the content of thought are called delusions. The commonest are delusions of persecution, where the patient may irrationally believe he is the subject of persecution (paranoid delusions), and these are often accompanied by auditory hallucinations. Delusions of a more bizarre nature (usually grandiose) can often be traced back to a more primary delusional experience.

Other patients may believe that certain situations have a particular significance to them and messages are being given to them (ideas of reference). Patients may have feelings of being controlled by outside influence (passivity feelings).

Disorders of perception

The most frequent disorders of perception are auditory hallucinations in the form of hearing voices. The patient may hear conversations between two or more voices and these may make him feel persecuted, as if the world is conspiring against him. The voice may be instructing the patient to do something. This can lead to dangerous or unpredictable behaviour.

Visual hallucinations are rare in schizophrenia. These are more often found in alcohol and drug intoxication.

Disorders of emotion
In acute schizophrenia, elation, ecstasy or depression may be present. These emotions usually settle to give way to the more characteristic emotional states. The emotional reaction and mood may be inappropriate (incongruity of affect), where the patient may laugh in the wrong places, or the wrong emotion is experienced for the given situation. There may be flattening of effect, where there is a lack of emotional responsiveness.

Disorders of behaviour
Withdrawal from normal social contact is a common symptom of schizophrenia. In its more extreme forms the patient might withdraw into a stupor-like state (catatonia) and become motionless, mute and not respond to external stimuli. This state can be interrupted by sudden outbursts of excitement (catatonic excitement). Frequently such patients show what is known as 'waxy flexibility' where the patient may hold his limbs in strange positions and keep these postures for long periods of time.

These states are now rare in their more extreme manifestations but are still seen in their milder forms.

Classification of schizophrenia

It is customary to classify schizophrenia into four sub-groups. This is now questioned by many psychiatrists because individuals seldom fall into such neat categories and therefore no hard and fast rule can be applied. There is often overlap between the various groups. In spite of this the different schizophrenic reactions do occur and their description remains valuable.

Simple schizophrenia
The onset occurs in adolescence and it is marked by gradual withdrawal from social contacts and loss of drive. Flattening of emotions and thought disorder may also be present. It is said that such disorders often go undiagnosed and untreated so such individuals may sink and drift into poverty, petty crime and vagrancy.

Catatonic schizophrenia
The onset occurs in early adult life. Patients can alternate between being withdrawn and mute to outbursts of sudden excited behaviour. This diagnosis is made less frequently in modern psychiatry, although catatonia still presents in milder forms. It is important to understand

that such patients have a clear appreciation of what is happening around them and will recall events lucidly when they recover.

Hebephrenic schizophrenia

Onset is in late adolescence. Emotional changes usually dominate the clinical picture. Such patients are usually preoccupied with pseudo-philosophical ideas, they are moody, sometimes giggly, fatuous and show characteristic incongruity of affect.

Paranoid schizophrenia

Unlike the above groups paranoid schizophrenia has a later onset, usually between 30 and 50 years. Delusions of persecution and auditory hallucinations are the typical symptoms. Unlike the other groups, the individual's personality is usually well preserved and does not disintegrate. Delusions may be 'encapsulated' and the patient behaves normally until his delusional ideas bring him into conflict with society. Such patients have hypersensitive personalities and respond to the most benign situations with suspicion. Prognosis is good, most cases respond favourably to neuroleptic drugs.

Burnt out schizophrenia

Patients suffering from this disorder consist largely of the late middle age group who have grown up in mental hospitals before the advent of effective medical treatment and community care. They are often institutionalised and emotionally blunted. Although they no longer respond to their delusions and hallucinations with the same intensity of their younger years they continue to experience them. Often they appear unkempt, neglect their personal hygiene and may still display peculiar or stereotyped behaviour.

Causes of schizophrenia

The cause of schizophrenia remains very much a matter of debate and continued investigation. No single cause is known. Evidence suggests an interplay of genetic, psychological and social factors, which seems to determine the development of the disease. People who have been adopted while still young and brought up by unrelated parents have been shown to have a high risk of developing schizophrenia. The closer someone is related to a patient with schizophrenia the higher the risk of them developing this condition.

Among the social and psychological perspectives of possible causes those of Bateson (1956) and Laing (1973) are significant. Bateson's 'double bind' theory is concerned with the ambiguity of communication between family members and has the following factors:

1. The individual has an intense relationship with a significant other carer (usually the mother, though it can be another close person).
2. The significant carer expresses two messages when making one statement, one message contradicting the other.
3. The individual cannot comment on the mutually contradictory messages and cannot withdraw from the situation or ignore the messages, thus creating a confusing conflict in the individual's mind which can only find resolution in madness.

R. D. Laing attempted to explain schizophrenia as a way of surviving the pressures of an abnormal family situation. Laing does not view schizophrenia as an illness but more as a 'behaviour label' for a certain kind of experience. Laing argues that it is necessary to accept these experiences as valid and seek to understand them as potentially meaningful; this is an existential truth. The practical effects of schizophrenia in our society are that the individual experiences a chaotic and distressing process which appears meaningless at the time. It seems to destroy their capacity for a full and meaningful life. Indeed, many schizophrenics are reduced by their illness into a deprived and marginal way of life.

The sociological view of drift theory has important implications for social work with the mentally ill. Some studies have been made on the nature of the relationship between social class and schizophrenia. These have illustrated a higher rate of sufferers from schizophrenia in central urban slum areas. The drift theory suggests that schizophrenics, as they become more disorganised and fragmented, drift into rundown areas where accommodation is cheaper and there is little social pressure upon them.

Goldberg and Huxley (1980) found that the occupations of male schizophrenics tended to be less well paid and prestigious than the occupations of their fathers. In their view social downward mobility indicated that as the mental illness develops the schizophrenic drifts into work which is simple and often well below his educational achievement. Unless there is effective social work and medical intervention, the schizophrenic may continue to go on to form the hard core of the destitute and vagrant population. Once they drift outside of the boundaries of helping agencies they can become deprived of effective treatment. They are then seen as tramps, rather than people in need of treatment.

Treatment

Treatment of the schizophrenic is primarily concerned with reducing symptoms by the use of phenothiazine drugs, which have an anti-psychotic effect. This simply means that these drugs are successful in suppressing some of the distressing effects of delusions and hallucinations. These drugs were first introduced in psychiatry in the early fifties, and have been used extensively ever since.

However, many patients tend to stop taking medication when they leave hospital or when they are beginning to feel better. In the majority of cases this can lead to relapse of the illness with a return to the former symptoms. Social workers must be aware of the effects and possible side-effects of such drugs and to be in a position to describe these to patients and to be able to liaise effectively with other professionals in the management of the patient's medication. (Medication is dealt with more fully in Chapter 9.) Default in medication is so common in schizophrenia that long acting phenothiazine injections have been developed to cope with the problem. Depot injections, such as Depixol and Modecate are given to the patient as an intramuscular injection by psychiatric nurses. These are given either in the patient's home or at the out-patients department.

Many of the drugs mentioned above can have unwanted side-effects. Drugs taken in large doses can produce drowsiness, tremor, restlessness, facial grimaces, protrusion of the tongue and chewing movements (tardive dyskinesia), also Parkinson disease-like symptoms, i.e. mask-like faces. Anti-Parkinsonian drugs, such as Disipal and Artane are very effective in counteracting such unpleasant side-effects.

Psychoanalysis

In certain cases, schizophrenic patients have been treated with psychoanalysis. This is a highly specialised and complex form of analytic treatment, and may last for many years. Interested readers are referred to the bibliography at the end of this chapter for further reading.

Social work with schizophrenia sufferers

Those suffering from schizophrenia are often struggling to cope with a self which they fear is falling to pieces and can no longer feel or think properly. As the boundaries of his mind become more uncertain the schizophrenic begins to doubt what is real and unreal and may begin to experience delusions and hear auditory hallucinations. By the time he reaches this stage of his illness his altered behaviour will be noticeable to all those who know him. He may become more withdrawn from family and friends, or alternatively he may be expressing bizarre behaviour which will be baffling and alarming. Schizophrenics in such a florid state are one of the most common groups of patients referred for hospital admission. Their unpredictable behaviour and strange beliefs can often arouse anxiety in those around them and produce a social crisis.

The approved social worker may be requested to be involved in the assessment of such an individual. This assessment will need to be in the light of the medical history and social circumstances of the individual and must consider both the need for hospital admission and the alternatives in the community. Social work with schizophrenia sufferers can be a delicate practice, for most fear emotional contact. Many situations which contain a high level of expressed emotion appear to produce a crisis or breakdown, and for this reason schizophrenics do better not living with their families at home. Social work intervention may need to be focussed on helping the patient and his family to separate from one another and so diminish some of the harmful interaction which can precipitate a crisis.

Research has shown that schizophrenics are extremely sensitive and vulnerable to their social environment. They tend not to be able to manage close personal relationships, and social care planning following a breakdown should take account of this and include the provision of an appropriate environment. For example, it might be less harmful and more conducive to his well being for the schizophrenic to live alone, rather than stay in a hostel containing a high degree of expressed emotion. Clearly schizophrenics share a common illness but are, of course, individuals and each will have his own needs. These broad principles are helpful as guidelines towards being aware of the particular care which this group of patients may require; but social workers must be flexible to meet the individual needs of the patient and his family. For example, the social environment should not be over stimulating nor under stimulating. It has been shown that an environment which is emotionally demanding and elicits strong feelings in the individual can soon produce a relapse. Conversely the environment which is under stimulating can produce further apathy and withdrawal.

The concept of the high degree of expressed emotion refers to the work done with schizophrenics and their families (Vaughan and Leff, 1976). They found that not only critical comments and hostility but also warm and overcaring, formed what is now known as 'high expressed emotion'. A patient who returns home to an environment which exposes him to these extremes has a greater risk of relapsing back into an acute schizophrenic episode. Social workers need to be mindful of this when making social care plans and need to consider the degree of 'expressed emotion' likely to be present in any particular situation and to help relatives, friends, wardens and sometimes colleagues to understand the nature of this in influencing the patient's behaviour.

The multi-disciplinary approach
Because of the very complex nature of the disorder, the management of schizophrenia needs a multi-disciplinary approach. Much of the behaviour of schizophrenia sufferers tends to be fragmented and this can lead to each professional receiving a different perception of the patient and his needs. It can sometimes seem as if organisations have taken on the muddle of their clients. It is by drawing together these perceptions that we can begin to get a more complete picture of the patient and thereby offer him the most appropriate care and treatment: social, as well as medical, human as well as institutional.

PSYCHOPATHIC DISORDER

'Psychopathic disorder means a persistent disorder or disability of mind (whether or not including significant impairment of intelligence) which results in abnormally aggressive or seriously irresponsible conduct of the person concerned.'

Part 1(2) Mental Health Act 1983

The psychopathic personality was first described as far back as 1835 by a Dr Pritchard when he wrote of 'persons of singular, wayward and eccentric character', and used the term moral insanity to describe such individuals. Since then various terms have been applied, such as sociopath, character disorder, psychopath and personality disorder. Here we will use the WHO definition.

Little is known with any certainty about the causes that form the psychopathic personality. Many believe it to be a failure to mature beyond the early explosive period of infancy, where the child has little or no capacity to contain his rages. Bowlby's work (1969) suggests that there was early emotional deprivation and a lack of a reliable affectionate relationship between infant and a significant person, which is generally but not necessarily the mother. Clinical practice normally reveals a high percentage of psychopaths from severely disrupted family backgrounds. Others have found abnormal physical factors, for example electro-encephalogram (EEG) findings which show unusual brain waves in many cases.

Definition: World Health Organisation definition of psychopathic disorder

Personality disorder characterised by disregard for social obligations, lack of feeling for others, and impetuous violence or callous unconcern. There is a gross disparity between behaviour and the prevailing social norms.

Behaviour is not readily modifiable by experience, including punishment. People with this personality are often emotionally cold and may be abnormally aggressive or irresponsible. Their tolerance to frustration is low; they blame others or offer plausible rationalisations for the behaviour which brings them into conflict with society.

The psychopath acts out his feelings so both he and his environment suffer. This behaviour invariably brings him into conflict with society. Most probation officers and social workers have a number of such clients on their caseloads. Because they seem unable to profit from experience attempts to help them are often unsuccessful.

Treatment
Conventional psychiatric treatment has little to offer this group of patients. If they are admitted to hospital they soon become disruptive on the ward and tend to have a destructive influence on other patients' treatment. They are best treated in special units with a therapeutic community approach. Here communication in the various groups enables patients to understand the effect their behaviour has on other patients. In feedback groups patients are encouraged to discuss each other's difficulties to gain understanding and insight. Emphasis is put on the events of the total living environment and by studying the problem created by the interaction, people are encouraged to talk out rather than act out their problems. Some patients develop more tolerance and develop a greater ability to control their impulsive behaviour which leads, in turn, to more satisfactory social functioning.

These centres are few and far between; the Henderson Hospital, for example, was the pioneer unit for such treatment. Prisons like Grendon Underwood also use this approach with some of their inmates. Many psychopaths are helped in the community by probation officers and social workers. Here the need to have modest aims can sometimes give the psychopath the opportunity to develop a relationship with a worker. This relationship may become the only good link the patient has with life and the importance of this should never be overlooked in terms of helping him to cope.

Puerperal psychosis

Some medical people have seen puerperal psychoses as specific psychiatric disturbances produced by childbirth in women. It is now generally agreed that these disorders are in essence no different to psychotic disorders which have already been described. Childbirth triggers off these psychotic conditions in persons who are already susceptible to such disorders and once they develop they present the same clinical picture seen in equivalent disorders and their care and treatment are similar.

The two main psychoses that can be precipitated by childbirth are schizophrenia and affective psychoses—mainly presenting a depressive picture.

Treatment

The main difference in treatment must, of course, be that it includes the infant. Where the mother is unable to cope because of either disorganised psychotic behaviour or depression, efforts should be made to admit them to mother and baby units together, to enable the mother to bond with her child. If the mother and infant are fortunate enough to receive in-patient care together, the mother is encouraged to participate in her full mothering role under supervision. Within such units the medical team is able to help with the precise nature of the difficulties and help the mother through them. Such units actively encourage an open door policy where the husband and members of the family are encouraged to visit and be part of the overall therapeutic programme.

REFERENCES AND FURTHER READING

Arieti S. (1981). *Understanding and Helping the Schizophrenic*. London: Penguin.

Bateson G. (1956). Towards a theory of schizophrenia. *Behavioural Science*; 1(4). In *Steps to an Ecology of Mind*. London: Granada.

Bowlby J. (1969). *Attachment*. London: Hogarth Press.

Clare A. (1976). *Psychiatry in Dissent*. London: Tavistock Publications.

Craft M. (1966). *Psychopathic Disorders*. Oxford: Pergamon.

Crowcroft A. (1967). *The Psychotic*. London: Penguin.

Goldberg D., Huxley P. (1980). *Mental Illness in the Community*. London: Tavistock Publications.

Hart B. (1962). *The Psychology of Insanity*. Cambridge: Cambridge University Press.

Klein M. (1980). On mental health. In *Envy and Gratitude and Other Works, 1946-63*. London: Hogarth Press and Institute of Psychoanalysis.

Klein M. (1981). A contribution to the psychogenesis of manic depressive states. In *Love, Guilt and Reparation and Other Works, 1921–45*. London: Hogarth Press and Institute of Psychoanalysis.

Laing R. D. (1973). *The Divided Self*. London: Penguin.

Leff J. P., Vaughan C. E. (1980). The interaction of life events and relatives' expressed emotion in schizophrenia and depressive neurosis. *Br. J. Psychiatry*; **136**: 146–53.

Mangen S. D. (1982). *Sociology and Mental Health*. Edinburgh: Churchill Livingstone.

Marks I. M. (1969). *Fears and Phobias*. London: William Heinemann.

McHugh P. R., Slavney P. R. (1983). *The Perspectives of Psychiatry*. Baltimore: Johns Hopkins University Press.

Palmer R. L. (1982). *Anorexia Nervosa: A Guide for Sufferers and Patients*. London: Penguin.

Priest R. G., Steinert J. (1977). *Insanity*. Plymouth: MacDonald & Evans.

Priest R. G., Woolfson G. (1986). *Minski's Handbook of Psychiatry*, 8th edn. London: William Heinemann Medical Books.

Richter D., ed. (1984). *Research in Mental Illness*. London: William Heinemann Medical Books.

Rosenham D. (1973). On being sane in insane places. *Science*; **179**: 250–58.

Rycroft R. I. (1980). *Anxiety and Neurosis*. New York: Raven.

Schneider K. (1959). *Clinical Psychopathology*. New York: Grune & Stratton.

Searles H. (1965). *Collected Papers on Schizophrenia*. London: Hogarth Press and Institute of Psychoanalysis.

Siegler M., Osmond M. (1974). *Models of Madness, Models of Medicine*. London: Macmillan.

Stafford-Clark D., Smith A. C. (1978). *Psychiatry for Students*. London: Allen & Unwin.

Szasz T. (1961). *The Myth of Mental Illness*. London: Secker & Warburg.

Vaughan C. E., Leff J. P. (1976). The influence of family and social factors on the course of psychiatric illness. *Br. J. Psychiatry*; **129**: 125–37.

Wing J. K. (1973). Social and familial factors in the causation and treatment of schizophrenia. In *Biochemistry and Mental Illness* (Iverson L. L., Rose S. P., eds.). London: The Biochemical Society.

Wing J. K. (1978). *Schizophrenia: Towards a New Synthesis*. London: Academic Press.

Chapter 2

Disturbances in Children and Adolescents

Paediatrics is the branch of medicine which specialises in the field of child care and childhood illnesses. Child psychiatry is specifically related to the mental and emotional difficulties which children and adolescents encounter. In addition there are other professionals interested in, and with responsibility for, child care. Most social workers will be acquainted with these, which include: GPs, schools, educational welfare departments, child guidance clinics (which are usually staffed by social workers but may be headed by a consultant child psychiatrist—who may, or may not be, a psychotherapist), police, adolescent units, and of course, social work departments themselves.

THE LEGAL FRAMEWORK

Under the law, a person's age is taken into account when deciding on their criminal responsibility as follows:

Age	Description	Responsibility
Under 10	Child	Not criminally responsible, although may be brought to court if in need of care or control
10–13 (inclusive)	Child	Criminally responsible *only* if it can be proved s/he knew that it was a wrongful act
14–16 (inclusive)	Young person	Criminally responsible
17 and above	Adult	Criminally responsible

For more detailed information on this area, interested readers are referred to works cited in the bibliography at the end of this chapter, especially *First Rights* (Rae *et al.*, 1979).

CHILDREN

By 'child' in this context we mean young people up to the time of puberty, which tends to occur around the twelfth year. This is generally regarded as the time when adolescence commences.

CHILD DEVELOPMENT

There are many schools of thought about child development. Some of the most important seminal contributions have been theories based on: psychosexual needs (Freud, 1975); cognitive development (Piaget, 1948); social interaction (Erikson, 1975); ethological factors (Lorenz, 1965); and learning behaviour (Skinner, 1972). Often these models devolve and become simplified to one of the most common controversies: 'Nature versus Nurture'. In looking at development, a helpful distinction has been made by Kahn (1971) between 'biological stages' (such as naturally arise during growth), and 'cultural stages' (such as are introduced by societal patterns).

Indeed, most authorities now view human growth and development as being dependent on a number of factors, which interrelate: no one factor being predominant. A combination of constitutional, early experience (including, according to recent literature, pre-birth experiences), parenting, social, cultural and economic factors, go to create what we call the 'personality'. Few would argue, however, that it was Freud who laid the original foundations for an understanding of childhood, through his empirical clinical work. For many centuries prior to this, children were seen as 'little adults', rather than as new and maturing individuals. Later writers, researchers and clinicians have built on Freud's early foundations.

Childhood psychiatric difficulties tend to occur when there is either a block in development, or an exaggeration of a normal process. In accordance with the principle of interrelationships of factors, such difficulties can be caused in many ways, and only a full assessment, using both medical, social and psychological expertise, will reveal the causes. For example, it is one of the tenets of family therapy that an unacknowledged difficulty within the family, or marital couple, will be expressed in the disturbed behaviour of either the family as a group, or one member—usually a child. It is for this reason that any child with a difficulty must be assessed in the context of his family and community, rather than as simply an individual with a problem: the 'identified patient'.

Developmental milestones

The so-called 'milestones' are the stages in a child's development which mark new abilities on their path to maturity. A rough guide to these is set out in Table 2.1. There is wide variation in the times that different children attain these milestones: thus when assessing a child's maturity other factors besides physical and mental ability will need to be taken into account: factors such as their general health and well-being, their emotional state, their relationship to the outside world, and conversely, the outside world's influence upon the child's immediate surroundings.

Table 2.1   Developmental milestones

Ability	Approximate age
Raise head: vocalising	3 months
Sit up: able to use cup	6 months
Crawling: worry when left alone	9 months
Stand unaided: first words spoken	1 year
Pick up things from floor: several words spoken	$1\frac{1}{2}$ years
Run: make phrases: clean	2 years
Ride tricycle: make sentences: sexual curiosity	3 years
Hop: speak well	4 years
Ride bicycle: dress and wash without aid	5 years
Puberty (menarche in girls)	12 years

CHILDHOOD PSYCHIATRIC DIFFICULTIES

Clinical syndromes have been described in attempts to classify and understand childhood difficulties.

Disorders

Emotional disorders can arise in the form of fears and phobias; depression; obsessions; hysteria; shyness; and elective mutism. Conduct disorders can be described as lying; fighting; and aggressive or destructive behaviour. Emotional and conduct disorders form the largest group of clinical syndromes. Conduct disorders may at first only come to the notice of parents or the authorities through some kind of deviant, or persistently 'naughty' behaviour.

Certain types of behaviour are of course often a combination of disorders. For example, school refusal is a disorder of conduct: refusing to attend school, which may be accompanied by delinquent behaviour whilst away from school. It normally has, however, an emotional component—in the form of a fear, a phobia, or an underlying depression. A further aspect of school refusal is, does the refusal lie in a fear of what is in the school—or does it lie in a fear of leaving home? This question would need to be addressed in the assessment, so as to influence the type of treatment pursued.

Psychoses

Psychoses are very uncommon and infrequent amongst children. Manic depression and schizophrenia rarely occur. When the symptoms of such illnesses seem to exist, they are more likely to be the mask of another, underlying difficulty. These serious forms of psychoses do not normally have their onset until the time of early adolescence, or later, in adult life.

Autism

Autism is the most serious psychological disorder of childhood, although it also occurs in comparatively few cases. Where it does occur, it can be observed in the earliest stages of the infant's life, characterised by complete withdrawal from his parents and the world. As the child grows older, he will be unresponsive, lack friends and the ability to make relationships, and without treatment will have a profound inability to speak or understand language.

Autism is more common in boys than in girls. The prognosis is not good. There is disagreement as to its causes: whether it is genetic predisposition, whether there are psychodynamic factors, or whether there are difficulties in the family functioning. Possible methods of treatment can therefore range from social skills training, behaviour modification, or psychodynamic techniques (such as play therapy).

Hyperkinetic syndrome

This is a difficulty marked by excessive and continuous activity, where the child cannot stay still for very long, and his concentration is very limited. This is more common than autism, but still comparatively rare, although recent research has indicated that it is an under-diagnosed complaint, and may occur in 1 in 200 children. Parents, in particular, need help to acquire necessary skills to understand and manage their children's excited behaviour, and must not be allowed to feel that they have failed because the hyperkinetic child demands knowledge and skills which parents do not normally have.

Tranquillising medication for such children is helpful in controlling some of their hyperactivity. It can also help to manage some of the more gross behaviour problems. There is a continuing controversy about the role of diet in treating this disorder.

Other specific difficulties

There are many difficulties which may arise either for very brief periods, or for a long duration. The more common ones are: difficulties in sleeping and eating (ranging from food fads to the serious illness of anorexia nervosa), tics, stammering, bed-wetting (enuresis), faecal soiling (encopresis), habits, psychosomatic problems, drug misuse, sexual worries, reactions to stressful and traditional life events, non-accidental injuries and their effects.

In addition, difficulties can arise in development where the child does not reach the normal milestones or perhaps surpasses them too soon. This would include such areas as slow learning, specific reading delay, speech delay, general underachievement—and the special problems which can arise for the gifted child (who may appear bored and disinterested because he is literally too far ahead of his peers).

Assessments

When called to assess a child, we are faced with an immediate problem: the child has not requested us to visit. Usually either his parents or his school will have requested our assessment. In addition, we may feel that we are assessing the child in order to help him. The child is more likely to feel that we have been called in by the authorities to chastise him.

In such a situation we would need to consider whether the type of problem is one more appropriately dealt with by an initial meeting with the child individually or together with his family. For example, a non-accidental injury investigation may be more sensitively dealt with by a one-to-one interview: a child with a school refusal difficulty may be more appropriately seen with his family, as any family conflicts will quickly emerge.

When interviewing children it will often be helpful to do so in a quiet room, away from everyday noise. In addition, toys or plasticine should be available to give the child something to fiddle with in order to help dispel tension. In child psychotherapy such tools are invaluable, often in terms of giving the therapist information about the child's internal world. For example, dark drawings with figures of destruction will be clear clues pointing towards a child's internal turmoil and fear.

Case illustration

A 12-year-old boy is referred to a special school unit with a learning difficulty and behaviour problems at school. He was very withdrawn and was always getting involved in fights—'started by others'. The social work assessment reveals that the boy is very timid—'wet' is the word which many people apply to him; and that his mother is very dominant and critical of the boy—yet at the same time, is reluctant for him to be involved with friends of his own age. His father avoids seeing the social worker. As the social work assessment progresses, it reveals that the boy believes he has a worm in his tummy eating his insides. How should the social worker view this boy? Clearly he is very miserable. What do his symptoms mean? In an adult, the idea of a worm in his insides eating him could be seen as a delusional belief, and therefore point to an incipient psychosis. This would be emphasised by the family members who related to each other in a way common to families with a member who becomes 'schizophrenic': a dominant, possessive mother; an absentee father; and an overawed, submissive male child. On the other hand, the feeling that the worm is eating him may point to a potential anorexic episode (starve himself to starve the worm); although anorexia is very uncommon in boys. The boy may have a fairly normal pubertal hypochondriasis; having heard somewhere that worms can live in humans, he's immediately afraid that they are in him. This would find fuel from feelings of being got at by external figures—the school, his mother—as if they too are in a way 'inside him', gnawing at his vitals.

There are no 'magical' treatment solutions. At this stage, it is sufficient that the social worker is aware of these dimensions and can monitor the boy's progress in the special school unit for which he is being assessed. What is important too is to pay close attention to the way that the boy develops and whether his belief in the worm continues, or alters. Through a sustained casework relationship, the social worker could do a great deal here subtly to influence the family dynamics, give the boy a greater feeling of self-worth, and help him separate from the influence of his mother.

Methods of treatment

It is a truism to say that all children are individuals and therefore any treatment plan must take strict account of this individuality. Its practical relevance is that for any presenting difficulty—such as a tic, or soiling—it will be important for the assessment to attempt to understand what that particular symptom means for that particular child. There can be no such thing as a dictionary of symptoms! Once such a tentative understanding has been gained, there are models of treatment which can be reviewed and adopted.

The main types of treatment that are used with success are individual psychotherapy, family therapy, group psychotherapy, individual and family casework, behaviour modification and medication. The type of treatment used must be considered alongside the venue: in particular, whether treatment is best applied in the home, with the family or whether the child needs to be removed from the home and into a day, clinical, or residential setting.

Individual psychotherapy

This is carried out in a one-to-one relationship between therapist and child. The child's parent will almost certainly be seen in an initial interview, and occasionally at subsequent interviews, but the essential therapeutic process will take place in private sessions between child and therapist. The therapist will usually use play techniques, encouraging the child simply to play, and describe his play. In older children and adolescents, play can be discarded, and verbal 'free association' employed ('free association' is the process where the patient says whatever comes into his mind without blocking any ideas or chains of association). The therapist makes comments on this material, interpreting from it the processes that are occurring in the patient's unconscious. Thus a child may make a plasticine mummy and daddy: the plasticine daddy hits the plasticine mummy and she falls down. The therapist may say something like, 'mummies sometimes get hurt by daddies'. Through the process of psychotherapy, the child gains a sense of internal equilibrium and relief, and the presenting symptoms disappear. Psychotherapy is a lengthy process requiring great commitment from therapist and patient (or the patient's parent in bringing the child-patient to the sessions). Psychotherapy aims at resolving the underlying causes of a child's difficulties.

Family therapy

Family therapists hold the view that when a child has a presenting difficulty, this is an expression of a problem within the family structure. Thus the family as a whole must be worked with, in an attempt to help them to understand and express verbally what the problem child has been expressing with his behaviour.

The advantages of family therapy over individual psychotherapy are that it takes away the stigma and burden of the 'difficult' family member having to carry the illness for the whole family. It is a fairly effective and economically fast form of treatment compared to individual psychotherapy.

The disadvantages are that it relies on commitment from the family—who are often under other pressures from a wide variety of sources including social and economic ones—and relies on their ability to be able to dismiss or present their conflicts. Often family dynamics may be so entrenched that we can only feel grateful that we have at least one family member, albeit the 'sick' one, who we are allowed to help. There may be a very strong vested interest in the family maintaining the status quo.

Group psychotherapy

This is a dynamic and interpretive therapy, undertaken in a group setting. The therapist makes interpretive comments to the group, about the group. This can also be quite a threatening experience, and should be structured carefully. It is not usually applied to children but is often used for certain groups of adolescents, mainly in clinical out-patient settings, and sometimes in special in-patient units.

Individual and family casework

This can be defined as the maintenance of a relationship with a client or family, providing through that relationship a sense of continuity and a facilitating environment, and playing a questioning or challenging role when that is appropriate. Social workers spend much of their time doing this: for many of our clients it seems to be a sort of 'lifeline'. But it remains ill-defined, with little acknowledgement from most sources. It is hard to quantify, and harder to assess in terms of outcome, care or change. It combines a variety of theoretical positions and political possibilities, and seems in many cases to be an appropriate method of work. This is discussed further in Chapter 12.

Behaviour modification

This is used very frequently, often under other guises. One of the clearest examples is the use of 'positive reinforcement' in the setting of a contract between client and social worker. The client and social worker each agree to perform certain acts, the mutual fulfillment of obligations resulting in, for the client, a release from his contractual duties (and for the social worker, we might add, a feeling of success).

It is often used for specific complaints, such as enuresis. In this example, a bell and a pad could be used to ensure that as soon as the child wets the pad on which he sleeps, he is woken by the bell. The child eventually associates wetting the bed with being woken, which leads on to him being able to wake before urinating, thus removing the enuretic symptom. This works on the principle of conditioning, or deconditioning, and its proponents claim great success in many areas, such as enuresis, fears and phobias, and certain sorts of antisocial behaviour.

Behaviour modification aims at removing the symptoms of a particular form of difficult or distressing behaviour. It does not attempt to deal in any way with the underlying causes of such behaviour.

Medication

This is rarely used for children's psychiatric difficulties. Readers are referred to Chapter 9 for a comprehensive discussion of these issues. For children, tranquillisers may be prescribed for short-term relief, but on the whole, longer term therapeutic intervention is non-drug based.

Venue

For dynamic, interpretive therapeutic work, whether individual or family, it is preferable for the venue to be away from home—perhaps in the therapist's office, or other quiet room without distractions. This emphasises the difference between the therapy and the home, and helps provide the patient(s) or client(s) with a container, in the form of the therapist's office and presence. If the family or individual lacks the desire to attend away from home it is unlikely that they will have the will to work towards understanding and achieve change.

In terms of placement, and in particular, whether a child should remain at home or be moved, then this would depend upon the type of difficulty, the family, and community setting. As a basic principle, the family is what the child knows, and therefore removal will inevitably tend to be disruptive. However, if his life or development was in severe danger—say through repeated non-accidental injuries or incest—then removal may need to be considered.

In terms of school refusal and learning difficulties, many local authorities now have special educational units, where children with these types of difficulty can be given intensive educational and casework time in order to overcome their difficulties.

CHILDREN OF MENTALLY ILL PARENTS

This is a client group for whom social workers can play a very helpful and important role, both in terms of ongoing support over a period of years, and also in times of crisis during hospital admissions. Children of mentally ill parents are in a vulnerable and sensitive position. They are at much greater risk than children in families where there is no history of, nor any current, mental illness (Rutter, 1966; Rutter *et al.*, 1977; Cooper *et al.*, 1977). The type of risk varies, and therefore the intervention will need to vary, according to whether the mental illness has been an ongoing difficulty for the parent—say in the case of a manic depressive illness or neurotic disorders which require long term therapeutic support—or whether the mental illness is clearly of short term duration—say in the case of puerperal psychosis precipitated by childbirth.

Long-term mental illness

In the case of a long-term illness, children will clearly need casework help in the form of an opportunity to explore and accept their parent's illness and its vicissitudes (its unpredictability, its confusion and misery). This will take many hours of patient counselling. Some children may not be able to speak about their feelings. Others will give the impression that they have no problems whatsoever. This can be a more worrying indication because it most likely means that the child is denying any problem, and that his worries have gone underground, and may resurface later. Hudson (1982) has pointed to the worrying implications of 'modelling', where the child models his behaviour on his parent—who may well be behaving quite bizarrely. Unless in physical danger, it is generally preferable to support such a family with the children staying at home: social workers will be guided on this by the wishes of the children, and the level of home care that the parent(s) are able to provide.

Short-term mental illness

In the case of a short-term illness or a crisis—in particular puerperal psychosis which is a severe psychotic episode of a time limited duration—there is less long-term casework to be done, but a reliance is placed on the statutory services, including the social worker to take control and manage the situation. It is at times of crisis that the issue of whether to remove the child or not becomes of prime importance. The psychotic parent may have a delusional belief about the child or infant, for example that their baby is a time bomb waiting to explode. In this situation the child may be at great risk. Removal from the mother could be indicated if the child were, say, two or three years old. Where the child is a new-born baby, then both mother and baby could be admitted together into a hospital unit, to allow bonding to continue, but in a supported and monitored setting.

The well parent

The other parent—the 'well' parent—can often be relied upon to manage a situation, and ensure that the child is compensated for any severe deprivation. However the social worker must be sensitive to their needs also, and support can be given to them. 'Support' can often be something as basic as an occasional telephone call, although it can be more. For example, the social worker can supervise meetings between a violent psychotic parent and his wife and children, to ensure that no harm comes to the wife and children, while still giving them the opportunity to keep in touch with their father.

Preventive measures

When a child has a mentally ill parent, preventive measures can be employed to try to ensure that any emotional difficulties in the future are minimised. For example, where a mother has a long-term psychotic illness such as schizophrenia and there is evidence that she had this when her child was born, then it may be appropriate for the social worker to discuss with the mother referral for the child to a child guidance clinic for out-patient individual psychotherapy. This can commence as early as the child's third year, and can help bring out and resolve any underlying unconscious difficulties. In addition, more immediately practical resources can be offered, such as nurseries, child-minding, playgroups, mother and baby and other self-help groups. In these ways, the child's mother may be given support from her peers without depriving her of her role as mother.

Unless resolved at an early stage, such difficulties may lie submerged until the time of puberty, which tends to act as a trigger for a replay of very early infant difficulties. This is one reason why many adult psycotic illnesses are precipitated around the time of adolescence.

ADOLESCENTS

We have seen that the child experiences rapid physical growth until later years of childhood where the pace slows down and early conflicts are for a time put aside. This is the calm before the storm. Adolescence is then marked by physical changes with the onset of puberty; this, together with psychological, academic and other pressures, come together to produce considerable stress. The young person's degree of disturbance and his ability to cope with it will be largely determined by the quality of care he has received as a child, and is now receiving, from his parents. For it is in adolescence that early childhood experiences and difficulties are reawakened, to come to the fore again.

All these rapid changes call for great powers of readjustment and inevitably lead in many cases either to emotional disturbance experienced internally as feelings, or acted out externally in behaviour. Most adolescents survive these stresses. Any interference in the individual's capacity to cope is usually temporary and related to some developmental stress already mentioned. The person may become depressed, feel anxious and have doubts about himself, but these pass and give rise to firmer plans about the future. Invariably this period is marked by alternative attitudes of wanting to become independent whilst at the same time seeking the care and support of parents. This is, therefore, generally a time of stress for parents too.

IDENTITY CRISIS

The central task of the adolescent is to establish the issue of his own identity. Before this time of transition, his identity will largely have been determined for him by his family, school and peer group. He will now be faced with shaping a role for himself, which often means a struggle towards independence, away from security: from parents to friends, from home to community. He will be seeking a place for himself in the adult world.

The crisis of identity is a particularly useful concept for those concerned with helping adolescents. It can give a focus and goal towards guiding them through their diffused and distressed (and distressing) behaviour, and into more mature relationships with their world. The behaviour problems expressed by the young person in his identity quest may vary from acts of destructiveness against family property, to complaints that he is unable to make friendships, to failing to fulfil academic potential at school. There may be experiences of emptiness, depression or isolation.

NEUROTIC AND PSYCHOTIC DISORDERS

We can now perhaps see how the normal stresses of adolescence can trigger off more profound problems which may have lain dormant since early childhood. These are usually related to failure in one of the developmental tasks, a failure which if not corrected by skilled help may begin to restrict the young person's emotional growth, and make attachments difficult. It is in this area that skilled psychotherapy is indicated.

Often these problems make it difficult for the young person to change his relationship with his parents, and he may reach adulthood with no close relationships. The adolescent may find it difficult to come to terms with his body, and in particular with his dawning sexual feelings. He may feel that his body is not really his own, that it is still the property of his parents, giving rise to guilt and disorientation.

Neurotic disturbances

Neurotic disturbance in adolescence has been differentiated by Laufer (1975) into two sub-divisions: 'simple neurotic disturbance', where the internal conflict does not appear seriously to interfere with the young person's life, but does reduce the level of his functioning; and 'serious neurotic disturbance', where there is a more long-standing deadlock within the person, interrupting his functioning. In both types of disturbance, the adolescent person does not lose contact with external reality, and is able to draw distinctions between the reactions of the external world, and his own mind.

It is important to bear in mind when assessing the extent of adolescent disturbance the age of the young person, and the 'age-appropriateness' of his behaviour. For example, a boy of 13 who is awkward and feels unable to allow himself to masturbate may be expressing temporary stress without it being a sign of permanent disorder. If the boy is still unable to masturbate at, say 18, this may be expressing a fear of his own sexual feelings.

A similar example could be the instance of a girl of 13 who is unable to go to a party because she is shy with boys, and feels herself to be unattractive. She may be showing signs of age-related stress. Whereas if the same girl is 18 and still unable to go to parties, she may be demonstrating an inability to allow herself to be a grown up woman; this, at the age of 18 would indicate an established disturbance, with which she would need help.

Psychotic disorders

The more severe forms of mental illness can occur in adolescence. It is critical to be able to distinguish between them, and normal adolescent problems. It must be emphasised that whilst the personality is still not fully formed, psychiatric diagnosis is notoriously difficult and unreliable; let alone indicative of prognosis and outcome. Made too definitively, it can lead to a premature and inappropriate labelling of the person.

Broadly speaking we should regard the adolescent as mentally ill where he has lost touch with reality. The psychotic type of disorder is usually more permanent and fixed than the transitory neurotic disturbance. The young person's thought, memory and movement are all affected. He will seem to be convinced that what his mind is creating —his 'internal world'—is true and real, irrespective of what is occurring in his home, school, work or social surroundings—his 'external world'.

Many people think that mental illness is obvious and that it requires little skill to be able to tell the difference between 'madness' and disturbed behaviour. Nothing could be further from the truth. The psychotic process can be a quiet and slow progression, and requires the expertise of a skilled psychiatrist to be able to form a diagnosis.

Schizophrenia and manic-depressive illnesses

Schizophrenia and the manic-depressive illnesses often have their onset in adolescence. It is therefore imperative to refer the adolescent for help where there are any indications that his behaviour suggests such mental disorders. Readers are referred to Chapter 1 for a discussion of the tell-tale signs of such illnesses.

OTHER DISTURBANCES

Among the other emotional disturbances that may occur and need to be referred for treatment are sexual problems (for example promiscuity, or concern and confusion about sexual identity), deliberate self-harm, obesity, solvent abuse, problem drinking or drug-taking. We have dealt with the more important aspects of these difficulties elsewhere in the present text.

Behaviour can also be indicative of underlying emotional conflicts. In particular this can be in the form of delinquent behaviour, such as burglary, stealing cars, compulsive lying, gambling, repeated drunkenness or theft. Where such behaviour is evident and persistent, a full assessment is indicated in order to understand and, if appropriate, treat a person's difficulties.

Treatment

Most adolescents come through their difficult passage and reach adulthood. Some, however, will need help to achieve this. In the case of the neurotic and psychotic individuals, psychiatric treatment will be essential to prevent the illness deteriorating and blocking further development towards maturity.

Most young people who need psychiatric help can be treated as out-patients with a combination of individual and group psychotherapy, and occasionally medication. In the more severe instances in-patient treatment may be indicated in special adolescent units where, parallel with treatment, the young person may have special tuition so that he is not left behind academically.

SOCIOLOGICAL PERSPECTIVE

In addition to the pressures created for the adolescent by his own feelings, there are of course, the difficulties which come, or seem to come, from others around him. These difficulties can, by their nature, seem incomprehensible to those closest to the young person. They can include such things as the pressure from parents to 'grow up', 'sort yourself out' or 'conform'. They might include the pressure from society to work, study or succeed. Such pressures may seem to the adolescent inappropriate to how he feels. They may seem to be of doubtful value at times of economic and cultural uncertainty.

One response to these pressures can be to become mentally ill. Or it can also take the form of an alignment with an alternative culture: the attraction of gangs, ideological movements, youth sub-elites, has been well documented, especially since the early 60s. One could list such examples as being the 'teddy boys', 'rockers', 'mods', 'hells angels', 'hippies', 'skinheads', 'rastas', and 'punks'.

This is clearly an area where psychological and sociological under-standing would need to merge in the process of assessment. For instance, a 14-year-old punk girl who sniffs glue may be telling us more about the cultural norms of the sub-group to which she has chosen to belong than she is about her own individual psychopathology.

REFERENCES AND FURTHER READING

Axiline V. (1974). *Dibs: In Search of Self*. London: Penguin.

Cohen D., Robins D. (1978). *Knuckle Sandwich*. London: Penguin.

Cooper S. F., Leach C., Storer D., Tonge W. L. (1977). The children of psychiatric patients: clinical findings. *Br. J. Psychiatry*; 131: 514–22.

Erikson E. (1975). *Childhood and Society*. London: Penguin.

Eysenck H., Rachman S. (1965). *The Causes and Cures of Neurosis*. London: Routledge & Kegan Paul.

Eysenck H. (1967). *The Biological Basis of Personality*. Springfield, Ill.: Charles C. Thomas.

Freud S. (1975). An outline of psychoanalysis. In *Complete Works of S. Freud, Volume 23*. London: Hogarth Press.

Fromm E. (1976). *The Sane Society*. London: Routledge & Kegan Paul.

Hall J., Jefferson J. (1979). *Resistance Through Rituals*. London: Hutchinson.

Haslam M. T. (1975). *Psychiatric Illness in Adolescence*. Guildford: Butterworths.

Hudson B. L. (1982). *Social Work with Psychiatric Patients*. London: Macmillan.

Kahn J. (1971). *Human Growth and the Development of Personality*. Oxford: Pergamon.

Kempe R. S., Kempe C. H. (1978). *Child Abuse*. London: Fontana.

Klein M. (1981). *Narrative of Child Analysis*. London: Hogarth Press and Institute of Psychiatry.

Lask B., Lask J. (1981). *Child Psychiatry and Social Work*. London: Tavistock Publications.

Laufer M. (1975). *Adolescent Disturbance and Breakdown*. London: Pelican.

Leech K. (1976). *Youthquake*. Tunbridge Wells: Abacus.

Lorenz K. (1965). *Evolution and Modification of Behaviour*. London: Methuen.

Miller D. (1969). *The Age Between*. London: Hutchinson.

Morgan R. (1984). *Behavioural Treatments with Children*. London: William Heinemann Medical Books.

Piaget J. (1948). *The Language and Thought of the Child*. London: Routledge & Kegan Paul.

Prior M. R., Griffin M. (1985). *Hyperactivity: Diagnosis and Management*. London: William Heinemann Medical Books.

Rae M., Hewitt P., Hugill B. (1979). *First Rights*. London: NCCL.

Roszak T. (1976). *Unfinished Animal*. London: Faber & Faber.

Rutter M. (1966). *Children of Sick Parents*. Oxford: Oxford University Press.

Rutter M. (1975). *Helping Troubled Children*. London: Penguin.

Rutter M., Herson L. (1976). *Child Psychiatry and Modern Approaches*. Oxford: Blackwell.

Rutter M., Madge N. (1976). *Cycles of Disadvantage*. London: William Heinemann.

Rutter M. (1977). *Maternal Deprivation Reassessed*. London: Penguin.

Rutter M., Quenton D., Yule W. (1977). *Family Pathology and Disorder in Childhood*. Chichester: Wiley.

Skinner B. F. (1972). *Beyond Freedom and Dignity*. London: Jonathan Cape.

Steinberg D. (1981). *Using Child Psychiatry*. London: Hodder & Stoughton.

Steinberg D. (1983). *The Clinical Psychiatry of Adolescence*. Chichester: Wiley.

Winnicott D. W. (1968). *The Child, the Family and the Outside World*. London: Penguin.

Winnicott D. W. (1980). *The Piggle: An Account of the Psychoanalytic Treatment of a Little Girl*. London: Penguin.

Winnicott D. W. (1982). *Playing and Reality*. London: Penguin.

Wolff S. (1971). *Children under Stress*. London: Allen Lane Penguin.

Chapter 3

The Elderly Mentally Infirm

About two thirds of referrals to Social Services Departments concern elderly people. Such requests may often be for practical help such as a home help or meals on wheels. These referrals can often conceal considerable unmet needs.

Before we begin to consider some of the mental disorders that affect the elderly, it is important to remind ourselves that old age itself is not a condition but a normal stage of life. People bring to it their own unique life experiences and personalities. One common factor old people share is a sense of depletion and this usually takes the form of diminished sight, hearing and physical mobility and lowering of living standards due to their reduced financial circumstances. All these problems can be compounded if the family has dispersed and the spouse has died leaving the old person alone and vulnerable. Many disturbances and mental disorders of old people have special features and for this reason we have decided to present them separately in this chapter.

AFFECTIVE DISORDERS

The most prominent affective disorder of old age is depression and it can carry a high suicide risk. This can be associated with some of the stresses of old age already mentioned. Depression can present extreme sadness or more subtly it can present many physical and confusional guises. These can take the form of vague physical aches and pains and preoccupation with the state of the old person's general health. Confusional behaviour resulting from a depressive disorder can sometimes be mis-diagnosed as dementia.

Depression varies in degree from feelings of sadness and a sense of loneliness to the most profound clinical type, although relatively rare in the elderly, called endogenous depression. The main characteristics of this disorder are loss of drive, everything is seen from a negative point of view, there is difficulty in concentration. The sufferer often feels worse in the morning when he usually awakes early and may gradually feel a bit better as the day proceeds. Preoccupation with bowel symptoms, including constipation, and hypochondriacal fears relating to cancer are common. Severe retardation can produce mutism, great difficulty in thinking and making decisions, and this can render the patient totally inaccessible. The patient often experiences marked restlessness and agitation.

HYPOMANIA

This can be the reverse side of the coin from depression. It occurs in about five to ten per cent of affective disorders in the elderly. The manic episode usually alternates with bouts of severe depression. In between these episodes of mania and depression there can be long periods of normality.

In the hypomanic phase the old person is usually bursting with ideas, energy and talkativeness. He is reckless, spends money he cannot afford on things he does not really want which can soon run up great debts and, if intervention does not take place, financial ruin. He may show considerable irritability, indeed this may be the first sign of his illness. If obstacles are put in his way or if he feels thwarted an aggressive reaction can be produced.

Manic patients do not eat or sleep very much and this can present considerable risk to their lives for they can soon wear themselves out. Another special feature which presents in the elderly manic patient at the outset is confusion which can lead to a mis-diagnosis of delirium. Paranoid ideas may be expressed and he may become frankly deluded and hear auditory hallucinations. Such behaviour can soon alienate him from family and friends.

Treatment

Although hypomania in the elderly is usually less severe than in other age groups, it is important to get it under control as soon as possible. Appropriate doses of major transquillisers such as Largactil and Haloperidol are given to reduce the excitement. Like hypomania in other age groups the elderly are best treated on an in-patient basis.

SENILE DEMENTIA

The commonest and most serious dementia is called senile dementia of the Alzheimer type (SDAT). In its rarer form, when it occurs before the age of 65, it is referred to as presenile dementia, and after that age, senile dementia. It is found predominantly in women. In the presenile type of dementia, there is a more rapid decline. The main characteristics of dementia are a decline in intellect, personality and behaviour. The most marked early symptoms are emotional disturbances, paranoid ideas, personality change, forgetfulness and loss of recent memory. The latter symptoms are due to the fact that the patient is no longer able to learn new information. Disorientation and an inability for conceptual thought are other prominent features. Memory of the remote past remains intact and this accounts for so many patients with this disorder dwelling on the past. In the early stages the person may have insight into his change in behaviour and his recent memory loss and this can lead to understandable distress for the patient and his family.

As the condition insidiously progresses, there is increased deterioration in social functioning to the point where the patient is unable to perform simple daily tasks, like dressing and feeding (this is called dyspraxia). This leads in turn to neglect of personal hygiene and general carelessness. Disorientation may then occur first in time, then in place and person, until he is unable to recognise his nearest and dearest.

Clearly it is extremely difficult for relatives to cope with old people in such a state. They will need considerable help, both in practical and emotional terms, to enable them to care for the patient for as long as it is possible in their own homes. This, of course, is providing it does not cause undue suffering to the patient and his family. It is often when the old person becomes incontinent, begins to wander and becomes aggressive that the social crisis occurs and relatives no longer feel able to tolerate or cope.

Aetiology

Over 80% of cases of presenile and senile dementia are of the Alzheimer type (SDAT). Although a strong hereditary factor is present, the cause of the disorder remains unknown. The brain of such an individual is one of diffused cerebral atrophy with enlarged ventricles. The disease progresses over five to ten years although this is variable and most patients live longer with good nursing and medical care.

Treatment
The main aim of treating patients suffering from irreversible dementia is to enable them to live as full and as active a life as possible in their own homes. When this is not possible because of gross disturbance and incontinence, residential care for the elderly should be considered or, if it is felt more appropriate, admission to hospital. Relatives will need to know the extent of some of the problems that the patient is likely to

present. Time is well spent in sharing with relatives and other professional colleagues the stress that such behaviour will place on all those involved.

Medical treatment will be focussed on diet, ensuring the physical condition of the person is maintained. Many psychogeriatricians do not like giving medication which sedates patients and may only increase their confusion. Certain drugs are, however, helpful in controlling restlessness and wandering and reducing the distress of the patient.

ACUTE CONFUSIONAL STATES

Delirium states are common in the elderly and can cause very disturbed behaviour. These may be the result of a number of stresses, usually physical but sometimes psychological. Physical stresses are usually caused by acute infections like pneumonia and these can soon be brought under control by the administration of antibiotics, often before the more florid states develop.

Although such conditions are usually treated in general hospitals, these patients may come the way of the approved social worker because of the disturbed behaviour associated with such conditions. The onset from normality to acute disturbance can occur within a few days. Confusion is often a prominent symptom, and this is more marked in the evenings and at night when the light fails and the patient is unable to perceive his familiar surroundings. The patient then becomes disorientated, bewildered and can experience terror as a result of frightening visual hallucinations. Disorientation is increased if the patient is transferred to another unfamiliar place. Memory for recent events may be lost and the patient may make paranoid interpretations of the events around him. His thinking is often disjointed and his talk may be either slow or, alternatively, accelerated. He suffers from clouding of consciousness, drowsiness and limited concentration. The patient is restless and he fails to grasp and maintain basic information. He may begin to roam the house or go into the streets, searching in his delirium.

Common causes of delirium states

1. Infections affecting the lungs, like bronchitis or pneumonia, and urinary infections which are common in the elderly.
2. Malnutrition.
3. Dehydration. Metabolic and endocrine disorders, for example diabetes, intoxication of drugs and alcohol, trauma of the head, hypothermia.

Among the psychological stresses which can produce delirium states, the most common are the shock of bereavement and moving home. Delirium states once diagnosed nearly always respond to treatment.

HUNTINGTON'S CHOREA

This is fortunately a rare inherited nervous disease which is caused by a dominant gene. This is an organic disorder. It does occur in much younger people but eventually leads to dementia. It is characterised by chorea, which are involuntary movements of the limbs, face and trunk. Alongside these physical disabilities, there is progressive mental deterioration leading to dementia. The onset of the illness occurs between 30 and 50 and the average length of life after onset is around 15 years, but this is of course variable. Often mental symptoms occur first and these consist of deterioration in habits, the patient often becoming careless and neglectful of his personal appearance. As the illness progresses there is failing memory, depression and irritability. Speech disturbance, stumbling and hesitation may cause difficulty in communication. Medical treatment by drugs consists mainly of trying to control the symptoms of restlessness so that the patient becomes more tolerable to himself and his family.

Social work with Huntington's chorea

Social work with families of people who suffer from Huntington's chorea should be focussed on support and counselling. Social work will be needed to help relatives to come to terms with the downhill prognosis of the illness. The illness can cause considerable distress to other family members. If these problems are anticipated, the family can be helped to begin to adjust to them.

The disease is due to a dominant gene and around 50% of offspring can be affected. Families need specialised help, called genetic counselling. A list of genetic advisory centres can be obtained through the Regional Health Authorities. There is a specialised self-help voluntary agency called COMBAT which offers information and support to patients and their families, and the local branch office may be found through either the Community Health Council or Citizen's Advice Bureau.

NEUROSES

Some of the most common symptoms of neuroses can be found in the elderly. These include bouts of depression, anxiety, hypochondriacal preoccupations, tension and irritability. The survey carried out in Newcastle (Kay *et al.*, 1964) found that neurotic disorders are continuations of neuroses which started in early adulthood, and are probably related to unfavourable situations in early life. Neuroses are not readily associated with the elderly and can therefore be overlooked. Although stress is seen as a prime factor in neurotic reactions, it is usually the actual experience of ill health in the elderly that acts as a trigger factor and increases anxiety in people who are already very vulnerable and anxious.

MULTI-INFARCT (ATHEROSCLEROTIC) DEMENTIA

This type of dementia is the result of a deprived blood supply to the brain which is usually caused by a series of little strokes, hardening and thickening of the arteries. Because parts of the brain are cut off from a supply of blood nourishment, the brain nerve cells die and cannot replace themselves, so such damage remains permanent. This disorder is often associated with high blood pressure and seems to affect more men than women. Average onset is around 60.

Unlike senile dementia there is often a sudden onset which produces episodes of confusion, slurring of speech and weakness down one side of the body. Sometimes the blood circulation is restored to the affected part of the brain which leads to some improvement and, in some cases, full recovery. However, most cases lead to the next episode within a matter of weeks or months. After a succession of such episodes there is often less recovery and the process leads to the characteristic 'step ladder' deterioration of personality with marked dementia.

Confusion in this type of dementia is unlike that found in other dementias. For example, the patient may be very muddled in the morning then become lucid and alert in the afternoon, only to return to wandering and disorientation in the evening. The patient is often very emotional and this may well be related to the fact that his personality is still well preserved until the late stage of his illness. Patients retain insight into their condition of failing memory and this can cause them profound depression and, in some cases, suicide.

As in other dementias, paranoid phases may be present. The patient will be sensitive to his memory deficit and questions posed to test a person's memory can often be met with a sudden turning away to avoid disclosing this deficit. This can be seen as an understandable defensive manoeuvre. Paranoid attitudes do not have the same elaborate system found in paraphrenia (see below) or other paranoid conditions of old age. They usually include those close at hand.

SCHIZOPHRENIA AND PARAPHRENIA

Schizophrenia in the elderly can be the result of a life-long illness which has persisted into old age. The person may continue to suffer from the severe residual defects of the disorder, blunted emotions, delusions and auditory hallucinations. Schizophrenia can also occur for the first time in the elderly and this condition is known as *paraphrenia*. Such disorders are usually predominantly found in women who live solitary life styles and who are often partially deaf. Although they may have always been regarded as somewhat eccentric they have not usually had a history of serious psychiatric illness.

The illness often occurs above the age of 65 and those presenting problems are invariably very bizarre with paranoid delusions relating to their neighbours. They are unlike the younger paranoid patient in the sense that the suspicions are localised to people upstairs or next door, and do not usually involve people in the wider world. Such paranoid delusions seldom alter but are held and sustained with strong intensity. These delusions are systematised and contain the most extraordinary sexual ideas and terrifying persecution.

Because of the troublesome effects of such a disorder it is unlikely to go unnoticed, for the person affected is likely to complain loudly about her imaginary persecutors. Request for rehousing is a common referral to social services but this is not likely to be very successful in the majority of cases, for such patients take their delusional system with them and soon begin to complain again with the same delusional ideas.

Like delusions in other disorders it is fruitless to argue with the person affected. It is important to acknowledge how frightened such experiences must make them feel and convey this to them without colluding with their delusions.

Treatment

Because it is often difficult to gain the trust of such suspicious individuals it is important to enlist the help of the community psychiatric nurse and the patient's GP. Medication along the lines given to paranoid schizophrenics is often very helpful in diminishing the intense persecution of the delusions and hallucinations that such people suffer. Intramuscular injections of either Modecate or Depixol can be given at prescribed intervals which can range from one to several weeks.

If the patient is acutely disturbed it may be necessary to admit him to hospital for assessment and treatment. Such patients often welcome this to give them some respite from their persecutors, but if an assessment can be made at out-patients this will be sufficient. Insight is rarely obtained and it is usually necessary for the paraphrenic to be under psychiatric supervision for the rest of his life. Day care can be a very helpful resource once the trust of the old person has been gained.

SOCIAL WORK WITH THE ELDERLY MENTALLY INFIRM

The approved social worker's role with the elderly will be primarily concerned with the mental disorders of old age, with special reference to assessment for admission to hospital, looking at alternatives and supporting elderly people and their relatives in their own homes. Ideally such assessments should be made by a multi-disciplinary team which should include a psychogeriatrician, the patient's GP, a nurse and the approved social worker. These should be made in the patient's home to enable everyone to become acquainted with the patient and his living situation. More than any other age group, social work intervention with the elderly must rest firmly on an early and accurate medical diagnosis. Old people are prone to many medical disorders which can affect their state of mind and a medical examination will determine the kind of treatment that will be required, both in a medical and social sense.

For example, if the elderly person is at risk as a result of an acute confusional state, he is likely to improve quite soon given the appropriate medical treatment. If, on the other hand, his muddled behaviour is the result of senile dementia, then it will be quite another story. Long-term care and management will be required to be planned and shared by medical and community services.

The cornerstone of caring for the elderly is to look after them in their own home for as long as is possible. Once a confused elderly person is transferred to a different living environment, he is likely to become more confused and disorientated. If any change in environment is planned, one will always need to balance this against what one can realistically expect relatives and neighbours to cope with when the elderly person's behaviour becomes too disturbed to be managed at home.

The front line carers will need support in practical as well as emotional terms if they are to be helped to continue to shoulder the burden of what will be a difficult task. All possible medical, nursing and social resources should be mobilised to ensure that maximum support is given. These could include day care, meals on wheels, laundry services, home helps and respite care. The approved social worker is likely to be called at a time of crisis when the carer feels angry and resentful and feels unable to cope any longer, or neighbours feel alarmed because the patient is wandering in the street at night or his behaviour is causing general concern.

The principal behaviour problems which produce a crisis or 'enough is enough' attitude are the old person's incontinence, wandering and aggressive outbursts. If the old person lives alone and is suffering from dementia, then he is destined for some form of institutional care. Clearly, without continued care such a person will deteriorate rapidly and will be impossible to cope with at home.

MEDICAL/SOCIAL WORK ASSESSMENT

This assessment can be carried out at home with the patient's GP, geriatric visitor or anyone who has direct contact with the patient. If the patient's condition is not known to his GP, he can usually assess the nature of the medical problem in the patient's home. It is seldom necessary to pursue endless investigations to determine the cause of the disturbance. However, further investigations should be made to rule out depression. The social worker's role in such an assessment may centre around four questions:

1. What has happened to the patient?
2. What has happened to his environment?
3. What has produced the 'enough is enough' reaction in the carer?
4. Will the carer be helped with extra support or has the point of no return been reached?

This last question will be the most difficult to answer. Most relatives want to care for their elderly at home. However, the constant demands that are made eventually evoke in the carer negative feelings of anger and resentment and these can make the carer spiral into greater resentment and despair. It is important to try to establish whether the carer is able to continue or not, often respite care can be organised.

REFERENCES AND FURTHER READING

Agate J. (1979). *Geriatrics for Nurses and Social Workers*. London: William Heinemann Medical Books.
Arie T. (1979). A positive approach to the care of old people with mental disorders. In *New Methods of Health Care*. Oxford: Pergamon.
Becker E. (1973). *The Denial of Death*. New York: Macmillan.
Brody E. M. (1977). *Long Term Care of Older People*. Atlantic Highlands: Humanities Press.

Carver V., Liddiard P. (1982). *An Ageing Population*. London: Hodder & Stoughton.

Gray B., Isaacs B. (1979). *Care of the Elderly Mentally Infirm*. London: Tavistock Publications.

Holden U. P., Woods R. T. (1982). *Reality-Orientation*. Edinburgh: Churchill Livingstone.

Jaques E. (1970). Death and the mid-life crisis. In *Work, Creativity and Social Justice*. London: William Heinemann.

Kay B., Beamish D., Roth M. (1964). Old age mental disorders in Newcastle Upon Tyne Parts I and II. *Br. J. Psychiatry*; 110: 146.

Kinnaird J., Brotherston J., Williamson J., eds. (1981). *The Provision of Care for the Elderly*. Edinburgh: Churchill Livingstone.

Kubler-Ross E. (1970). *On Death and Dying*. London: Tavistock Publications.

Levy R., Post F. (1982). *The Psychiatry of Late Life*. Oxford: Blackwell.

Mann A. H., Graham N., Ashby D. (1984). Psychiatric illness in residential homes for the elderly: a survey in one London borough. *Age and Ageing*; 13: 257–65.

Pitman L. (1978). *Death and the Family*. London: Faber & Faber.

Pitt B. (1982). *Psycho-Geriatrics*. Edinburgh: Churchill Livingstone.

Post F. (1965). *The Clinical Psychiatry of Later Life*. Oxford: Pergamon.

Raphael B. (1984). *The Anatomy of Bereavement*. London: Hutchinson.

Rowlings C. (1981). *Social Work with Elderly People*. London: Allen & Unwin.

Whitehead T. (1971). *In the Service of Old Age*. Aylesbury: H. M. & M. Publishers.

Williams I. (1979). *The Care of the Elderly in the Community*. London: Croom Helm.

Chapter 4

Suicide, Violence: A Danger to Themselves or Others?

SUICIDE AND SELF-HARM

There have been many studies of suicide and self-harming behaviour. The origins of such behaviour still give rise to controversy: should we differentiate between a 'completed' suicide, as against an 'attempted' suicide? Is an attempt at suicide more of a 'cry for help', than an act aimed at self-annihilation? Is a suicidal person in some way disturbed, or may there be a valid intention behind their action—for instance, in the case of a terminally ill person who wishes to die sooner rather than later? These are some of the difficulties facing us when we consider suicide and self-harming behaviour.

A more helpful way of viewing such behaviour, however, can be to see both completed and attempted suicides as attacks on the self, the aim being to annihilate some part or all of the self which is felt as threatened, or threatening. To separate suicide from self-harm may be to minimise the intentions of the person and underestimate the powerful destructive and unconscious forces that are at work.

RESEARCH

American research (Miles, 1977) has shown that all American suicides are undertaken by people with one or more of the following conditions: depressive illness, alcoholism, schizophrenia, neurosis, personality disorder and drug addiction. Diagnosed mental illness accounts for the highest proportions: 90% in American studies (the highest proportion amongst people suffering from depression; followed by alcoholism); and 93% in British studies. The significance of these risk factors for social workers is clear. They should be taken into account when making assessments. In addition, life events can precipitate suicidal feelings. These include bereavement or other loss, separation, and physical illness. Recent statistics issued by the Samaritans in the UK indicate that suicide is increasing amongst young men (under 20 years of age) but decreasing amongst young women. In general in the UK, suicide seems to be on the increase: 5000 recorded instances in 1983—a fifth more than in 1975.

SOCIAL WORK ISSUES

Approved social workers are required to assess whether or not the client needs to be admitted to hospital. In order to do this, they must be able to draw together information on both psychiatric symptoms and social conditions. There is evidence from research that the most vulnerable members of the community are those people who are ageing, depressed, isolated, alcoholic or people facing situations from which they can envisage no future (examination failure, bereavement, financial loss, terminal illness). Admission to hospital does not necessarily decrease the risk of suicide. Therefore, even if it is recognised that the patient is a suicide risk, the approved social worker has to consider whether to make an application for compulsory hospital admission or if some other alternative plan of help can realistically be used. Environmental support, medical help, meaningful social activity and casework need to be fully explored. To elicit a client's agreement to work on a problem which a client has identified is tantamount to the beginning of a move away from suicidal feelings.

RISK FACTORS

Suicidal feelings are very powerful and can be transmitted in an unconscious way to those around, including the social worker, giving rise to feelings of negativity and helplessness in even the most professional of professionals. This will be discussed in more detail in Chapter 12. In practice one defence against this may be to keep in mind a check list, both of risk factors and areas to investigate in the assessments. Such factors as a combination of two or more of the following will alert the social worker that the person concerned needs help and, possibly, hospital care:

1. Ageing.
2. Loneliness.
3. Bereavement.
4. Family history of suicidal depression.
5. History of previous suicide attempts.
6. Recent onset of a depressive illness.

7. Symptoms of depression which increase vulnerability (persistent insomnia, ideas of guilt/worthlessness).
8. Florid psychosis.
9. Alcoholism or drug addiction.

Amongst the elderly, minor illnesses like the onset of deafness, limited sight and movement restriction, can have a disproportionate effect as they tend to increase loneliness and feelings of isolation. Living alone, being widowed, moving into new districts, all these are socially isolating circumstances which have been found to be more prevalent amongst suicides than amongst the rest of the general public. People suffering from organic brain symptoms may also be a high suicide risk, especially when in the early stages of the illness. When any of these events are found in addition to severe depressive symptoms, then it is necessary to consider this person to have a very high suicide potential. In addition, people suffering from chronic painful illness, especially where there is a history of anxiety or depression, or when they are unable to cope or are unaware of the diagnosis, are high risk. Personality attributes may also be relevant in the assessment of suicide potential and these can include impulsivity, spontaneous depressive swings of mood, the use of alcohol or drugs and aggressive tendencies. It has also been suggested that rigidity and an inability to cope with new situations, fixed attitudes to death and strong religious conviction can, in fact, increase the suicide potential at times of additional stress. Strong faith is often a protection against taking one's own life but when strong faith is linked with severe depression about personal value and worth, this can be associated with overwhelming guilt and be a source of acute and unbearable stress.

ASSESSMENT

The origins of suicide will probably always remain a mystery. Those who do not die, who harm themselves in a self-destructive manner, may be 'attempted suicides', or their self-destructive act may have a different significance: self-injury rather than self-destruction. The most common experience, however, seems to be the existence of profound despair in the suicidal person. As soon as despair is recognised it is important to be able to indicate this recognition to the sufferer. The social worker will beware of giving trivial reassurances, no matter how tempting, as these only confirm the client's fears of not being understood, being alone, alienated, or not being taken seriously. The social worker has to try to convey to the client that he is sensitive to his pain and wants to help. Clients with overwhelming feelings of despair, helplessness, hopelessness, failure and exhaustion, seem unconsciously to need to get those around them to join in with their despair. An example of this is the person who spends a lot of time trying to get the people around to agree that there is no use in trying to help, no necessity to make further appointments to meet because 'things will always be the same' and who needs to convince the social worker and doctor that 'nobody can ever help'. As depression usually has a finite duration it is important to refuse to go along with this kind of thinking and to be able to explain why. The use of antidepressants, alongside social work help, involving the GP, the social worker and, if appropriate, the community nurse, can be a way to help the client to emerge from a seemingly bottomless pit.

PLANNING INTERVENTION

It is never easy for a client experiencing suicidal feelings to be able to communicate feelings of despair, particularly at a first meeting. The social worker carries the responsibility of trying to create an atmosphere whereby the client can trust him and be able to express painful feelings. This may mean that the social worker will need to be frank and honest about why he has been asked to see the client, or alternatively it may lead the social worker into being a fairly silent, but listening, presence. Often, in crisis situations, the worker and doctor are under pressure to act quickly. This may be essential in cases of violence, may not be so essential when dealing with a potential suicide. Once the immediate risk has been removed, such as getting the client away from the window or removing dangerous objects, such as tablets, then it may be more important to stay physically with the client and allow time to discover what the despair is all about. The client needs to be encouraged to talk and at the point of crisis should not be left alone. In an emergency situation it is sufficient to be guided by the client's own evaluation of what is worrying him. Do not try to find out about early life situations unless this is volunteered: although it is important to help the client to express painful feelings it is crucial, in an assessment interview, to try to discourage too much irrelevant discussion which clouds the main problem and only serves to confuse and fatigue both the social worker and the client. It is more relevant to focus on the client's experience of the present moment.

The client may be only too ready to dismiss all offers of help in what he feels is a hopeless situation. This may have the additional motive of testing out the social worker's ability to tolerate despair. The social worker has to be aware of this and to keep the focus on what is happening and avoid other issues. The client's feelings of despair will most likely have been passed on to relatives and neighbours and it is important to disentangle this and to focus attention upon the needs of suicidal client, although, of course, the family may need support which can be offered when the immediate crisis has been understood and shared.

Chronic painful illness, especially when the source of anxiety or depression, can be a central issue as also can living alone, being widowed, moving into a new district, feeling isolated, unemployed, without loved objects. All of these life experiences are important factors in heightening feelings of despair. They need to be recognised, shared and not avoided. The client may express feelings of being dislocated from any goodness within and could well need to go into hospital in order to be safe.

Short, planned interviews help the patient anticipate the future. If possible, it is good practice to agree the length of the interview with the client so that he can begin to use the time constructively and the social worker, by making an appointment to see the client again, can demonstrate that despair need not overwhelm. Subsequent interviews can then be focussed on helping the client to express feelings of despair. Ideas of suicide should not be avoided if the client wants to talk about this. The client can be encouraged to think about ways he thinks he could be helped and some sort of contract between social worker and client may be possible. Practical issues must be discussed as must arrangements to meet again, talk, listen and 'be with' the client. The GP must be involved, particularly where there are anxieties about health matters. The social worker needs a good knowledge of out-patient treatment, day hospitals and day centre facilities, together with the ability to mobilise practical help such as home helps, visitors, day centres, help of a financial nature, and community resources to help relieve isolation.

HOSPITALISATION

If suicide risk is severe and all help is refused, or if the client is too deeply depressed to respond to any offers of help, it may well be necessary to apply for compulsory admission to hospital. This is an exceptional circumstance but does arise where depressive symptoms have reached psychotic severity. A client expressing suicidal ideas or refusing to talk, eat, move out of his room or wash, may be unable to accept any help offered and the doctor and social worker may feel that they have no alternative but to recommend hospital admission, as they cannot be sure that he will not harm himself. A decision has to be made in the light of the social situation, the medical recommendations, and the ability of the client to accept help or to believe that anything in his life can change.

When expressing suicidal feelings, a covert feeling amongst some of our clients may be that their death will somehow punish those around —family members, friends, ourselves. It is important to draw this feeling out if it is present. The accompanying fantasy may be that in some way a part of the client will survive the suicide and 'see' the grief on the faces of the survivors. It needs to be made clear to the client, in these situations, that they are the ones who will be most damaged by their suicide—because they will die. In reality, there will be no victorious satisfaction for them afterwards at the grief of others.

SCHIZOPHRENIA

People suffering from schizophrenia are high on the list of those who need protection from self-injury. This is particularly the case where hallucinations and delusional ideas are clearly related in content to suicide or self-harm. The person may be hearing voices which command him to kill himself. He may have beliefs that his body contains poison which needs to be destroyed by burning. In these psychotic states the person is unlikely to accept help, because it contradicts their own internal demands.

A RIGHT TO DIE?

A number of research findings highlight the high suicide risk found amongst the isolated and elderly population. They can present the social worker and doctor with a particular ethical problem which connects with broader issues to do with the right to die concept. Within the law, approved social workers have a clear duty to make an application for hospital admission for assessment or treatment if the patient 'ought to be so detained in the interests of his own health or safety or with a view to the protection of other persons'. The law, therefore, to which social workers are accountable, takes the view that the protection of someone from killing himself is as much a medical and community responsibility as is the protection against any other cause of death for which there are preventable measures available.

Taking these factors into account, how do we help a client with such feelings about the quality of his life? One focus could be on why he has been allowed to become so alone and isolated. The positive aspect could be to look at ways in which life could be lived in a less solitary way. Another focus could be simply to allow the client to express anger about the quality of his life, to say how awful it is, and why; and for these to be acceptable feelings to have.

Clients who are rational and therefore able to make a considered choice between life and death and express a clear wish to die may be very few. For a social worker to condone and go along with someone's wish to die because it seems to them to be a preferable alternative to life is to take a very serious course of action. The social worker in this situation must examine his own motives, and ask himself if they have become invaded by their client's sense of despair or ambivalence. It could be said that we do not know enough about death to counsel it, or allow it, as an alternative to life.

VIOLENCE

Most social workers are no strangers to violence. Many of the clients with whom they work have suffered deep levels of emotional deprivation which will have engendered in them a low threshold of tolerance and a limited capacity to absorb and contain frustration. Social and economic stress in later life can combine with these factors, leading to a sense of inarticulate rage inside the person. As a consequence, the social worker often meets clients who readily exhibit verbal and physical aggression.

The common image of the 'mad' man or woman is of someone who seems to possess a superhuman strength and who is prone to outbursts of unprovoked and uncontrollable physical violence. Such a frightening image seems to have been around since the beginning of time and may have influenced the kind of treatment and attitudes society has adopted towards the mentally ill. Social workers need to challenge this image and bring some reality to bear if they are to dispel and diffuse the sense of danger that such a primitive image evokes.

The aggressive drive within us all takes many forms. Used in a positive way it enables us to master our environment and makes survival and progress possible. In its more negative manifestations it can fuse with hatred and produce great cruelty. History abounds with examples of both the positive and negative aspects of aggression. Indeed, there are some people who cannot come to terms with their aggressive drive and who are unable to integrate it into their personality. They can become severely incapacitated as a result of not being able to use such energy in a creative or positive way. In gross forms they may be regarded either as maladjusted or suffering from mental disorder.

The aggressive drive turned inwards against the self is a cause of much depression and can lead to suicide. In other cases, especially in the schizoid person who withdraws from his aggressive drive and other strong emotions, there is emotional coldness and flatness. In yet others and particularly the paranoid person, hostility is projected either to a specific person or an organisation, leading the paranoid person to believe himself to be the subject of unwarranted persecution. The psychopath, on the other hand, deals with his aggression in an impulsive way by 'acting out' the hostility and may resort to violent crime or cause suffering to himself and to other people.

In this context, it is now perhaps important to define 'violence' and what we mean by it. Here we use the word to describe aggressive behaviour which is potentially dangerous to the person's physical well being or to other people. Do the mentally ill exhibit a greater degree of violence than, say, members of the general population? There is no evidence that this is the case. The underlying personality of the individual appears to be the determining factor and this seems to transcend any particular psychiatric diagnosis. Clearly it would be dangerous to make generalisations or to try to predict when or where a patient will exhibit violence.

VIOLENCE AND SCHIZOPHRENIA

The largest group of psychotic patients the approved social worker or community psychiatric nurse is likely to come in contact with are those suffering from schizophrenia. They may present as withdrawn but sometimes their behaviour and conversation can be bizarre. They often entertain delusions which have a violent component. Paranoid schizophrenics, in particular, experience persecutory delusions and live their lives in a constant sense of grudge, persecution and impending violence. Because they project their hostility on to the outside world their delusions often consist of being hounded by special organisations or individuals.

Case illustration

For example, a woman in her mid-life is described by her husband as always having had a 'suspicious nature'. She was in the third year of an Open University course and was very upset when her brother died. She stopped studying and became convinced that the Gestapo were looking for her. She talked about her 'skin being made into a lampshade' and had threatened the neighbour in the opposite house and said that he was watching her through binoculars. She had drawn the curtains in all the rooms of the house and refused to turn on the lights. For two weeks she had not left the house and was talking about burning it down with her husband and children inside to avoid 'capture and interrogation'. She refused to see her doctor and was suspicious of all approaches from her husband and friends.

Psychoanalytic theory views this sort of behaviour as retaliatory. Having externalised her aggression by projection (and thereby given herself a sense of safety), the client begins to live in fear of it returning to her in a boomerang fashion, thus inducing terror and a state which has been described as 'retaliatory dread'. Clearly the approved social worker should be concerned that this group is the most dangerous of the schizophrenics. It has been observed that victims of schizophrenics' aggression are often people who have personal contact with them such as relatives and friends.

Catatonic schizophrenia

A particular group, the so-called catatonics, now quite rare in clinical practice, form a potentially dangerous group of patients. In their excited state they may suddenly emerge from their withdrawn stupor and become violent. Nevertheless it must be restated and stressed that it is the patient's personality as it was before the onset of his illness (the 'premorbid' personality) that will indicate his tendency or otherwise to violence whilst experiencing his illness.

THE AGGRESSIVE PSYCHOPATH

Perhaps the most dangerous patients are those described as 'aggressive psychopaths'. The Mental Health Act defines them as:

'Psychopathic disorder means a persistent disorder or disability of mind (whether or not including significant impairment of intelligence) which results in abnormally aggressive or seriously irresponsible conduct on the part of the person concerned.'

Part 1(2) Mental Health Act 1983

These patients are not regarded as suffering from a mental illness but as having a 'disordered personality' where aggressive impulse control is often very diminished or absent. They often display great emotional immaturity, lack of foresight and ruthlessness in meeting their own needs, with little appreciation of the feelings of those around them. They often abuse alcohol and drugs, seem to play with life and death, and cause great suffering to themselves and others. This can be seen as using violence as a way of problem solving.

Social workers, probation officers and doctors will be readily familiar with such individuals. They must be regarded as potentially the most violent group of patients in psychiatry. However, they can only be compulsorily admitted to hospital for treatment if 'in the case of psychopathic disorder or mental impairment, such treatment is likely to alleviate or prevent a deterioration of his condition' (Clause 3(2)b, Mental Health Act 1983). Consequently, where a patient has had a number of hospital admissions and has been described as a 'psychopath', violent situations involving him should be handled by the police and the courts. Social workers do not have the physical and legal resources to handle such unpredictable, but potentially dangerous, clients.

Social workers should be aware of evidence of morbid jealousy as this has important relevance to the understanding of violence. This condition often culminates in severe assault, suicide or murder. As a symptom of psychiatric disorder morbid jealousy can be found in schizophrenia, depression and personality disorder. Characteristically, morbid jealousy appears in one partner who imagines the spouse as being unfaithful. Frequent rages occur which result in violent behaviour. Morbid jealousy is frequently cited as the motive for murder or sexual attack. The dynamics of marital friction are complex but in acute cases of jealousy, where there is also a history of mental disorder, complete separation of the married pair has to be considered. This may not prevent the disturbed partner from repeating the situation with a second partner, who may well also become a potential victim. It may be that there is also a particular psychological component in some people which is attracted to such a potentially jealous partner. This needs to be watched for when making assessments and recommendations.

THE ASSESSMENT OF RISK

The problem for the social worker is that in many incidents it may not be possible to know much about the background or personality of the patient. This is particularly the case when a crisis occurs at night and access to files and people who know the patient is impossible. The approved social worker has to try to obtain some information about the history and personality of the patient as this could be the key to understanding the present problem. For example, it is important to know if the patient is epileptic and whether his behaviour could have a physical base. A history of alcoholism or drug abuse may well be an important factor in violent behaviour; or it may be a reaction to a frustrating or unexpected life event. The approved social worker has a clear duty under the Act to make an application for admission to hospital where it is felt that the person is a danger to himself or to other people and where hospital assessment is the most appropriate way of helping the patient.

Clearly, it is not only the mentally ill and the criminal who experience violence. More commonly it is expressed in close relationships within families and in marital disputes and one of the tasks of the approved social worker is to try to differentiate between 'normal' violent outbursts, which also need to be understood in a cultural context, and those which are a complication of acute mental illness. Essentially, violence can be viewed as a deep sense of helplessness which is felt in the face of a perceived threat; this can be experienced by the individual as a fear of loss of control. The patient's anxiety can be felt as so overwhelming that reasoning is blocked. He then feels unable to manage stress with his normal coping mechanisms and resorts to violence as a way of desperately trying to establish his self-control. The threat of a compulsory admission may well play into his worst fears that he no longer has control over his own life. For this reason, the approved social worker must not be indecisive or ambivalent about using authority, as uncertainty can play into the patient's fears and lead to an escalation of violence. Clarity and firmness may actually be very helpful to patients experiencing fearful panic.

The patient may need control as he may fear that he can no longer contain his own destructive forces and someone has to take over for him. In such cases he may well be relieved that he is being taken to hospital. In the *Case illustration* above, the lady who would not leave the house because of her fears of capture and torture became calm and quiet when the social worker and doctor told her firmly that the ambulance was outside the house and she was going into hospital.

People often act out their inner turmoil through violence when they fear that their normal coping mechanisms are blocked. Their increase in fear and loss of control reach a catastrophic peak in their minds and they feel they have no other way of expressing their extreme helplessness. One of the most important skills of the approved social worker is the capacity to enable the client to feel 'held' and understood. He has to be helped to put into words what he is feeling, rather than to act out the anxiety he is suffering, speak with words rather than with aggression. This is, of course, easier said than done and must be practised in the context of making the assessment situation as safe as possible for all concerned. It is quite foolish for the social worker to believe that an assessment can be made when the people involved, including the social worker, are afraid that they might be physically assaulted. It is particularly important in a potentially violent situation for all the professionals involved to share the assessment interview and, if necessary, to have the police nearby. Approved social workers and doctors must avoid falling into the trap of regarding themselves as omnipotent. Others around may expect the social worker and doctor to have some magic formula which will change the lion into a lamb merely with the right choice of words or sleight of hand. The social worker may find it helpful in such situations to be aware of what is being put into them by others: the projective identification that is being carried out. This will certainly help the social worker to keep his head, but it may also help him to bring clarity and some sense of ease to what may well be a very dis-eased situation.

Case illustration

Violent behaviour has to be seen in context of what has preceded. For example, John, suffering from schizophrenia, attended the DHSS office for assessment for his supplementary benefit. His social worker had arranged to be with him but got caught up in the traffic and as a result was late for the appointment. By the time he arrived at the DHSS office John was in a violent rage and all the DHSS staff were extremely worried and were becoming hostile towards him.

This young man, because of his illness, had got into a financial mess and had been without money for several days. This had aroused in him a mounting sense of frustration and the DHSS interview had become the last straw.

Such incidents will be familiar to most social workers and clearly John's outburst of rage could be seen simply as his innate vulnerability in the face of what he saw as another obstacle to his need for money, without the support of his social worker. It is easy to understand why he felt unable to hold out any longer.

Each situation will present its unique set of problems, but, where violence is present, it is helpful to observe the following:

1. Take the patient and his threats seriously.
2. Immediately consider the safety of potential victims who may be involved in the assessment.
3. Obtain as much previous history and information as possible.
4. If necessary, summon help to make the situation 'safe' for everyone.

5. Avoid heroics.
6. Help the patient to talk.
7. If an admission is necessary, do not delay. Prompt action should be taken.

It is critical to take threats of violence seriously, especially if there is some evidence that the person making the threats is actually going to act upon them. For instance, someone who is threatening to 'kill the Pope' is not a threat to the Pope unless he has a plane ticket to Rome or is attending a mass rally where the Pope will be present. The case of the murder of John Lennon is an example of threats not being treated seriously. The murderer had a long history of psychotic disorder and often talked about his overwhelming hatred of John Lennon and intent to kill him. He began to follow reports of Lennon's activities and bought himself a gun. He took a train to New York and waited every day outside the hotel where Lennon was living. His threats had not been taken seriously as he was regarded as 'deluded'. However, when he began actually to do something positive about acting out his projected hatred, he certainly was a 'danger to others'.

Violence evokes violent feelings in others and it is important to recognise this and not to deny them by becoming fearful on the one hand, or defensive or nonchalant on the other. These attitudes will only escalate aggressive behaviour. The social worker has to try to steer between the two extremes and adopt a quiet but firm stance. The social worker should try to approach the underlying anxiety and fear of loss of control and convey this understanding by saying something like 'I can see that you are upset and I want to help you'. When the patient becomes threatening, answers should be unprovocative, such as 'I will not let you lose control and harm yourself or anyone else'. It can be more helpful to try to establish this rapport before beginning to talk about the client's problems.

Safety of potential victims

It is helpful to remove potential victims from the assessment situation, or make the situation safe enough for everyone to remain and take part in the interview. It will be important to try to elicit whether the patient's anger is diffused or whether it is directed towards some particular person. Has the patient a particular plan in mind? Has he a method? Such questions will help to establish the seriousness of the *intent* of the violence.

Patients who suffer systematic delusional symptoms and are making arrangements to kill their persecutors should be regarded as extremely dangerous. Obviously such potential victims will need to be safeguarded, as discussed above in the John Lennon case.

Previous information

Files on patients may not always be readily available. However, every endeavour must be made to seek information on the patient and to try to discover how he has dealt with stress in the past and the likely pattern of his aggressive behaviour. It is also important that the social worker writes a full report of the assessment outcome in the file for further reference.

Summon help

In situations where there is a risk of violence the police should be alerted. The social worker and doctor have to decide what part the police should play in the assessment but it is important that should an admission be necessary it can be effected without delay. The police can be very helpful and indeed essential in extreme violent situations. They represent control, clearly identified by everyone, and are empowered to act decisively. Violent patients invariably react to the presence of the police and become calmer. This usually enables the patient to feel safer and makes him more accessible, thus allowing both doctor and social worker to make an assessment, without they themselves becoming too unduly afraid. Conversely, the social worker should not be afraid to summon help. We must be aware of our limitations, and not try to be heroic where it is clear that there is either a serious element of risk, or a largely unpredictable source of potential violence.

SUMMARY

In this chapter we have discussed the meaning of violence and aggression for our clients and its relationship to ourselves. It has been suggested that the roots of aggression lie within us all, and there is no direct and simple relationship between mental illness and violence. The determinants of any form of violent behaviour lie in the personality and social origins of the whole person. Nevertheless, there are severe and frightening manifestations of violent behaviour and it is emphasised that where there is an unpredictable or unknown element, social workers need to exercise caution, being neither too heroic, nor yet too fearful.

REFERENCES AND FURTHER READING

Suicide and self-harm

Alvarez A. (1972). *The Savage God*. London: Penguin.

Barraclough B., Bunch J., Nelson B., Sainsbury P. (1974). A hundred cases of suicide: clinical aspects. *Br. J. Psychiatry*; **125**: 355–73.

Catalan J., Marsack P., Hawton K. E., Whitwell D., Fagg J., Bancroft J. H. J. (1980). Comparison of doctors and nurses in the assessment of deliberate self-poisoning patients. *Psychological Med.*; **10**, 483–91.

Department of Health and Social Security (1984). *The Management of Deliberate Self-harm*. In Local Authority Social Services Letter HN(84)25, LASSL(84)5 (December, 1984).

Farmer R., Hirsch S., eds. (1980). *The Suicide Syndrome*. London: Croom Helm.

Fox R. (1973). *The Management of the Suicidal Patient*. London: Constable.

Gardner R., Hanka R., O'Brien V. C., Page A. J. F., Rees R. (1977). Psychological and social evaluation in cases of deliberate self-poisoning admitted to a general hospital. *Br. Med. J.*; **ii**: 1567–70.

Gardner R., Hanka R., Evison B., Mountford P. M., O'Brien V. C., Roberts S. J. (1978). Consultation-liaison scheme for self-poisoned patients in a general hospital. *Br. Med. J.*; **ii**: 1392–4.

Gardner R., Hanka R., Roberts S. J., Allon-Smith J. M., Kings A. A., Nicholson R. (1982). Psychological and social evaluation in cases of deliberate self-poisoning seen in an accident department. *Br. Med. J.*; **284**, 491–3.

Gibbons J. S., Butler J., Urwin P., Gibbons J. L. (1978). Evaluation of a social work service for self-poisoning patients. *Br. J. Psychiatry*; **133**: 111–18.

Greer S., Bagley C. (1971). Effect of psychiatric intervention in attempted suicide: a controlled study. *Br. Med. J.*; **i**: 310–12.

The Hill Report (1968). Joint Sub-Committee of the Standing Medical Advisory Committees. Hospital treatment of acute poisoning. London: HMSO.

Holding T. A., Buglass D., Duffy J. C., Kreitman N. (1977). Parasuicide in Edinburgh—a seven year review. *Br. J. Psychiatry*; **130**: 534–43.

Kennedy P. (1972). Efficacy of a regional poisoning treatment centre in preventing further suicidal behaviour. *Br. Med. J.*; **iv**: 255–7.

Kreitman N., Philip A. E., Greer S., Bagley C. (1969). Parasuicide. *Br. J. Psychiatry*; **115**: 746–7.

Miles C. P. (1977). Conditions predisposing to suicide: a review. *J. Nerv. Ment. Diseases*; **164**: 231–46.

Morgan G. T., Pocock H., Pottle S. (1975). The urban distribution of non-fatal deliberate self-harm. *Br. J. Psychiatry*; **126**: 319–28.

Report from the Child and Adolescent Psychiatry Section (1982). The management of parasuicide in young people under 16. *Bull. Coll. Psychiatrists*; **October**: 182–5.

Stengel E. (1975). *Suicide and Attempted Suicide* London: Penguin.

Topp D. O. (1979). Suicide in prison. *Br. J. Psychiatry*; **134**: 24–7.

Trethowan W. (1979). Suicide and attempted suicide. *Br. Med. J.*; **2**: 319–20.

Violence

Ardrey R. (1967). *The Territorial Imperative*. London: Collins.

Arendt H. (1979). *On Revolution*. London: Penguin.

Benedict R. (1959). The natural history of war. In *An American Anthropologist at Work* (Mead M., ed.). Boston: Houghton Mifflin.

Berkowitz L. (1962). *Aggression: A Social Psychological Analysis*. New York: McGraw-Hill.

Carthy J. D., Ebling F. J. eds. (1964). *The Natural History of Aggression*. London: Academic Press.

Ciba Foundation (1966). *Conflict in Society*. London: J & A Churchill.

Ellul J. (1969). *Violence*. Oxford: Mowbray.

Engels F. (1942). *The Origins of the Family, Private Property and the State*. New York: Int. University Press.

Frankl V. (1964). *Man's Search for Meaning*. London: Hodder & Stoughton.

Freud S. (1913). *Totem and Taboo*. London: Hogarth Press.

Freud S. (1915). *Instincts and their Vicissitudes*. London: Hogarth Press.

Freud S. (1933). Why war? In *Collected Works, Volume 22*. London: Hogarth Press.

Fromm E. (1960). *The Fear of Freedom*. London: Routledge & Kegan Paul.

Fromm E. (1977). *The Anatomy of Human Destructiveness*. London: Penguin.

Jaques E. (1970). Guilt, conscience, and social behaviour. In *Work, Creativity and Social Justice*. London: William Heinemann.

Jung C. G. (1974). The undiscovered self. In *Collected Works, Volume 10*. London: Routledge & Kegan Paul.

Jung C. G. (1977). Psychological types. In *Collected Works, Volume 6*. London: Routledge & Kegan Paul.

Kaada B. (1967). Aggression and defence: neural mechanisms and social patterns. In *Brain Function Volume 5* (Clemente C. D., Lindsay D. B., eds.). Berkeley: University of California Press.

Lorenz K. (1962). *On Aggression*. London: Methuen.

Prins H. A. (1979). A danger to themselves and others. *Br. J. Social Work*; 5: 297–309.

Skinner B. F. (1977). *Beyond Freedom and Dignity*. London: Penguin.

Storr A. (1974). *Human Aggression*. London: Penguin.

Tournier P. (1978). *The Violence Inside*. London: SCM Press.

West D. J. (1965). *Murder Followed by Suicide*. London: William Heinemann.

Wynne Edwards V. C. (1962). *Animal Dispersion in Relation to Human Behaviour*. Edinburgh: Oliver & Boyd.

Yates A. (1962). *Frustration and Conflict*. London: Methuen.

Chapter 5

Problem Drinkers and Drug Users

Problem drinking and drug abuse have much in common. Both can lead to serious harm to the individual's mental and physical well being and have wider repercussions affecting his family and society. Many problem users suffer deeply from underlying difficulties which seldom receive the attention they need because of the presenting problems of their alcohol and drug abuse. Both seem to have 'addictive personalities'; that is to say that they use these drugs to try to obliterate and avoid facing their problems. Problem users can create a confusing impression: on one hand, an inevitable sense of destructiveness; on the other, a sense that taking the drug represents a kind of incorporation of goodness which the user feels he lacks.

PROBLEM DRINKERS

Many practitioners now believe it is not helpful to use the disease label of 'alcoholism', for it can denote an incurable illness which may prevent people from seeking help. The term now in popular use is 'problem drinker' and we will use this term throughout this chapter. Having said that, we must understand more clearly the term 'alcoholism', for it has a specific meaning which is defined by the World Health Organisation. Alcoholics are defined as:

'those excessive drinkers whose dependence on alcohol has attained such a degree that it shows a notable mental disturbance or an interference with their bodily and mental health, their interpersonal relations and their smooth social and economical functioning or who show prodromal signs of such development.'

Alcoholism was mainly diagnosed in the middle years when evidence of damage caused by alcohol becomes more apparent. However, there are now growing and disturbing signs that it is being diagnosed in younger people.

One of the central difficulties in trying to help problem drinkers is their reluctance to admit that they have a drinking problem in the first place. Often they deny the extent of their drinking until the damage it causes can no longer be ignored by the patient and his family. All social workers will be aware of the manifold areas of problems which exist for the problem drinker, and the impossible demands and pressures that they put on their family and friends, until they eventually lose them. In more severe cases the problem drinker finally becomes a vagrant person with a derelict life.

THE THREE MAIN STAGES OF PROBLEM DRINKING

Excessive drinking stage

Here drinking is increased in social situations to obtain relief from tension. This is gradually followed by an increase in alcohol tolerance which requires more drinks to attain the same effect. At this stage, the individual begins to experience guilt about the level of his alcoholic intake, which further heightens his anxiety. Drink has now become a necessity for him in order to cope both socially and in his place of work.

Alcohol addiction

The drinker avoids discussing his intake and begins secret drinking. Self-control is lost where drinking becomes so compulsive. This is followed by a reduction in his performance at work and in absenteeism. A whole range of social consequences then arise which can include social isolation, aggressive outbursts, family break-up, neglect of diet, depression and, in many cases, suicidal attempts. Indeed, the problem drinker is a high suicide risk.

Chronic alcoholism

By the time the person enters this stage, certain characteristic features begin to emerge. When, for example, alcohol is withdrawn or reduced, a severe reaction in the form of shakes, agitation, and visual and auditory hallucinations of a frightening nature occur, e.g. insects crawling over the skin. This, in its more severe stage, is known as delirium tremens (DTs).

The classical picture of chronic alcoholism which produces a dementia is known as Korsakoff's syndrome or psychosis. This is characterised by selective memory loss. The patient often confabulates by making up stories to cover up his memory deficit. In addition, the person is often confused and disorientated, is fatuous and often has a grandiose view of himself. All such conditions can be arrested, but the damage done to the brain is irreversible.

SOCIAL WORK WITH PROBLEM DRINKERS

Because problem drinkers deny their difficulties, they are often referred, and brought reluctantly, by relatives or friends for treatment. Often, when they have reached this stage, they have lost their job through drinking, have an unhappy marriage or are already divorced, or have housing problems with complicated financial difficulties.

The problem facing social workers trying to help the problem drinker is one primarily of motivation. Since success in any treatment regime requires the drinker's cooperation, many early attempts at helping him may fail because of denial and poor motivation.

Problem drinking by itself is not sufficient grounds for detaining anyone under the Mental Health Act 1983. Section 1 of the Act states:

'Nothing in Sub-section 2 above [which defines mental disorder] shall be construed as implying that a person may be dealt with under the Act as suffering from mental disorder, by reason *only* of promiscuity or immoral conduct, sexual deviacy or *dependence on alcohol or drugs*.'

However, in paragraph 14 of the DHSS Memorandum, it states:

'It is recognised that alcohol or drug abuse may be accompanied by or associated with mental disorder. It is therefore possible to detain a person who is dependent on alcohol or drugs if they are suffering from a mental disorder arising from or suspected to arise from alcohol or drug dependence or from withdrawal of alcohol or a drug, if all the other relevant conditions are met.'

This would seem to imply that those suffering from psychiatric disorders induced by alcohol, or disorders associated with its withdrawal, *could* be compulsorily detained *if* their health is at serious risk.

Treatment
Because of his poor motivation the problem drinker can be difficult to engage in treatment. Often the patient too is aware of this and suffers from great doubts about his ability to cooperate in any treatment plans. This will, of course, be especially true if he has had several earlier

attempts at withdrawal which have failed, leaving him with the feeling that no-one can help him. Setbacks in his daily life, and a return to heavy drinking to help him cope, will only have reinforced his fear of withdrawing from alcohol. Behind the so-called denial carried out by the problem drinker, lie such fears and humiliation.

Social workers need to be sensitive to these issues if they are to help the problem drinker to feel understood and helped. The casework relationship with such individuals and their families can centre on these matters. Once established, this relationship can be helpful in persuading and offering information about possible treatment approaches. Often such basic information can dispel the terrifying ideas that people may hold about treatment regimes. For example, the media has created many distorted and dramatic images which can often deepen the terror and guilt of the sufferer.

'Drying out' is one of the commonest procedures for withdrawing the individual from alcohol. This is done on an in-patient basis in a hospital or special unit. The patient is gradually withdrawn from alcohol and is given tranquillisers to alleviate some of the distress associated with the withdrawal symptoms. Attention is paid to his general physical condition and such issues as vitamin deficiency, common in heavy drinkers, is treated by giving large doses of vitamins by injections.

Once his general condition begins to improve and the acute symptoms subside, the patient will need to make a decision about his long-term care, because 'drying out' is the first step towards a longer treatment regime. This phase is critical. Many problem drinkers drop out at this stage, thinking that they have conquered the problem, only to relapse later with a bitter sense of failure once again. It is in this period that the patient needs a full psycho-social assessment of the difficulties which may be causing and perpetuating his drinking problem. Several treatment approaches are available and would need to be geared to the individual needs of the patient.

Group and individual psychotherapy, aimed at helping him to locate and work at the unconscious conflicts, would be useful to help resolve the problems they generate. Clearly this treatment requires the cooperation and long-term commitment of the patient. Problem drinkers may need extra help in the form of medication to help combat some of their anxieties in having to cope with their lives without alcohol. To this end, tranquillisers are often prescribed to help them to handle daily stress.

Another useful aid is the drug antabuse (Disulfiram) which is often prescribed to those patients immediately after the 'drying out' phase, who fear going back to treatment. This drug causes the body to feel revulsion when alcohol is taken. Unpleasant symptoms such as giddiness, flushing of the face, and general feelings of distress are experienced and this occurs each time the patient drinks after he has taken antabuse. In many cases the patient cannot be relied on to take this medication. There is now a simple implant operation which introduces the drug into the body, and this acts over a period of time. Clearly this kind of treatment can be unpleasant and if it is to be successful, it requires the motivation and cooperation of the patient, who may need this kind of stand-by to aid him in his recovery.

Aversion therapy, which is based on the principles of behaviour modification, is sometimes used to produce in the problem drinker an aversion towards his drinking. This technique employs apomorphine (an emetic drug—given to produce vomiting) which is given to the patient with his favourite drink. This causes him to vomit and feel disgust, and through this treatment repeated over a period of time, he begins to associate drink with very unpleasant experiences.

Self-help groups such as Alcoholics Anonymous (AA) and Accept are perhaps the most successful methods of treatment from the long term point of view, for many groups provide supportive social network support and are available twenty four hours a day. Many patients find it difficult to come to terms with the more extrovert approach adopted by Alcoholics Anonymous, but there can be little doubt that this organisation has helped countless numbers of problem drinkers in giving them hope and a new start in their lives. Accept is a newer group which was established in the UK about 10 years ago. It offers more innovative ways of helping by offering a wider range of social contacts including day centres and befriending.

PROBLEM DRUG USERS

As in the term 'problem drinker' there is an increasing move away from the term 'drug addict', towards 'problem drug user' to describe the drug-dependent individual. The Advisory Council on Misuse of Drugs, a government appointed body, in its two reports 'Treatment and Rehabilitation' and 'Prevention' (1982, 1984, respectively) set the tone for recent developments by stressing the need to view the problem of drug dependence as *problem* orientated, rather than *drug* orientated. Although problem drug users may, as a group, present similar patterns of difficulties, each drug user is an individual, needing to be assessed in the light of his own particular psycho-social problems.

It is helpful to differentiate between drug *dependence* and drug *abuse* in the following way: to define *dependence* as the means by which the drug taken creates physical and psychological dependence with an increasing tolerance, and where, if the drug is withdrawn the person will experience withdrawal symptoms; *abuse* may then more appropriately be used for the instances where the drug taken does not produce dependence.

The World Health Organisation definition of drug abuse is as follows:

'A state of periodic or chronic intoxication, detrimental to the individual and society, produced by repeated consumption of the drug. Its characteristics include an overpowering desire or need to continue taking the drug and obtain it by any means, a tendency to increase the dose; psychic and sometimes physical dependence on the effects of the drug.'

Drug dependence in the UK in the past usually involved those who had easy access to drugs and medicines, such as professionals like doctors, chemists and nurses, or patients who were prescribed the therapeutic use of opiates. Now the situation is quite different. There has been an enormous increase in drug taking over the last two decades in this country, often involving young people. Over the last two years, for example, the use of heroin has escalated dramatically. With greater availability and its relatively low cost, it is now distributed in towns throughout the country, making it accessible to a general population. The current cost averages between £5 and £10 per day for the average user's illicit supply.

Unlike the early heroin addicts there is a move away from intravenous injections (main lining) and all the fatal hazards associated with that ritualistic procedure, such as infections and embolisms. Now the fashion seems to be to sniff or smoke heroin. This usually takes a little longer to work but avoids the risks already mentioned.

Habituation to heroin usually develops rapidly and once it takes hold of the individual it follows a predictable pattern. There is an increase in tolerance which requires an increase in dosage to achieve the same effect. If the drug is not available, unpleasant withdrawal symptoms can occur. The life of the problem drug user soon becomes a journey from one dose to the next. If money is not available to meet the cost of the drug, he may resort to all kinds of measures, including illegal methods.

Problem drug use is important for several reasons. Firstly, in itself it can often be an expression of individual and group disturbance. Secondly, and very relevant to the work of the approved social worker, is the way in which certain psycho-active drugs can induce psychotic reactions which can closely resemble disorders such as schizophrenia.

Some of these drugs can be detected in the urine tests of the patient. Others can not and this can lead to difficulty in making a diagnosis and prescribing treatment. The psychiatrist must then rely on the patient to ascertain whether or not he has taken drugs.

Here we will describe some of the major psycho-active drugs that are taken and the abstinence symptoms or side-effects that can occur. We will also look at the way in which drug-induced psychoses can sometimes occur in the vulnerable individual. These drugs can be taken separately or in combination with other drugs.

BARBITURATES

Under their trade names of Tuinal, Seconal and Nembutal, these were commonly used as sleeping tablets before they were discovered to have addictive qualities. It is now recognised that they are very dangerous drugs. They can cause confusion and ataxia (whereby the person's gait and speech resembles that of a drunken person). Withdrawal needs to be gradual under medical supervision as fits can occur. These drugs are also the commonest drugs used in suicide.

AMPHETAMINES

These were commonly called 'pep pills' and used to alleviate depression before the introduction of antidepressant medication. They were also prescribed for slimmers to help curb their appetite. Taken in large doses they can produce a form of psychosis indistinguishable from schizophrenia. When this drug is withdrawn, the patient may need help with the distress and depression associated with its abstinence.

THE HALLUCINOGENIC DRUGS (e.g. LSD, MESCALIN)

Although not drugs of addiction, they can be very dangerous. For example, they can produce states of mentally altered awareness, with heightening and distortion of sensory perception. Many accounts have been recorded of people under the influence of such drugs who believed that they could fly, often with tragic consequences. The person can also experience feelings of all-powerfulness and hallucinations, and in persons prone to psychoses, it can produce schizophrenic-like reactions. 'Trips' caused by these drugs are unpredictable. In some cases, experiences can recur and these are known as 'flashbacks'. It is of interest to note that mescaline was originally used by South American Indians to induce states of altered consciousness, to which they attributed spiritual value.

COCAINE

This was once a fashionable drug amongst those who could afford it. It is now rapidly becoming a street drug. It is often taken by sniffing 'decks' (finely shaved strips) of the drug. Cocaine allays hunger and produces increased energy, alertness and euphoria. Taken in large doses it can make the person delirious and cause him to suffer visual and tactile hallucinations—such as insects crawling over the skin. Some of these features can resemble a psychosis.

CANNABIS INDICA

Taken in sufficient amounts this drug can produce vivid dreams or visual hallucinations together with a disorder of time and space. In the average amount, it is mildly euphoriant, increasing auditory sensibility and dreamy states. In *ganja* and *bhang* there may be a higher concentration of cannabis and this may lead to a profounder effect on the user.

INHALANTS

Although glue sniffing has received a great deal of publicity in recent times, the inhaling of substances like nitrous oxide, ether or other anaesthetics has been documented as occurring amongst dentists and doctors.

A wide variety of household and industrial products can be sniffed. Perhaps the most popular at the present time is glue sniffing, particularly amongst groups of young people. The inhalation of organic solvents can produce delirium and hallucinations, and can lead to liver damage. Asphyxia can also occur, usually as a complication of using plastic bags in the sniffing process.

Solvent abuse can be used as part of a group culture (e.g. amongst punks or other adolescent groups). However it can also be undertaken by individuals as an isolated and solitary activity. The former will need to be assessed in terms of the group process and the sociology of the group culture. The focus in the latter instance will more appropriately be the need and probable disturbance within the individual.

BENZODIAZEPINES (VALIUM, MOGADON)

These are primarily prescribed for anxiety and insomnia and are effective drugs used in this way. However, they are now regarded as drugs of dependence and countless numbers of people take them regularly. The problem drug user may use them, either by themselves or combined with other drugs. People who have been on these drugs for long periods of time are likely to experience withdrawal symptoms if they try to give them up. It has been discovered, for example, that feelings of depression, anxiety, nausea and panic have been felt when these drugs have been withdrawn.

Treatment

The treatment of problem drug users follows a similar pattern to that for problem drinkers. Most health areas have regional drug dependency clinics where users can receive help with their drug problems and underlying difficulties. These clinics are staffed by doctors, nurses and social workers with special expertise in the care of problem drug users. Doctors, for example, are approved by the Home Office under the Misuse of Drugs Act 1971, and only they are allowed to prescribe for the user.

Essentially, treatment is designed to contain and help the patient over the withdrawal phase by replacing the drug of dependency with a milder tranquilliser to alleviate the acute distress symptoms. In the case of heroin withdrawal, a substitute drug called Methodone is given until the withdrawal symptoms subside. Because these can include delirium, acute panic, hallucinations and physical symptoms, Methodone is given to ease the transition and deal with the abstinence from heroin.

It must be borne in mind that the drug user's fear of withdrawal effects may keep him dependent on the drug. It is important therefore to be able to reassure him that treatment can help minimise his distress. In the case of the stimulant drugs such as amphetamines which can leave the user feeling sluggish and depressed, the user may benefit from antidepressant medication and tranquillisers to cope with both the anxiety and depression of coming off the drug.

Often, problem drug users approach the clinic not with the intention of treatment, but to obtain a supply of drugs. Usually each person is assessed and the doctor in charge, with his special experience, is able to establish the particular needs of each patient.

These clinics are run on a multi-disciplinary approach and counselling, individual and group work are used to help the user understand the nature of his problems. The withdrawal of drugs can often be a long and arduous process requiring patience on the part of the patient and staff. Relapse is frequent and in order to use this constructively, the withdrawal treatment needs to be seen as a learning process so that each relapse can be understood in context.

The mid-1980s have witnessed the resurgence of a 'moral panic' in the drugs field, with calls for greater penalties for drug-pushers, greater resources for treatment centres, and even the use of troops in the war against drugs. It remains to be seen how these calls will be followed up and, more importantly, what preventive measures will be taken to make drug abuse a less attractive option for alienated young people.

INDICATIONS OF DRUG ABUSE

The following signs are commonly regarded as indicators of drug abuse. However these signs may indicate other difficulties, not necessarily drug abuse (for instance, they are in many cases part of the normal process of adolescent development!). Thus it must be borne in mind that to elicit a true diagnosis a full medical assessment must be made. Such a procedure would include urine analysis and other specific tests.

The signs are as follows: sudden mood changes; unexpected irritability or aggression; lost appetite; loss of interest in normal day-to-day activities; bouts of drowsiness; unusual instances of lying or furtive behaviour; money or belongings disappearing; unusual smells, stains, or marks on the body or clothes or around the person's home; unusual powders, tablets, capsules, scorched tinfoil, needles or syringes.

REFERENCES AND FURTHER READING

Bourne P. G. (1976). *Acute Drug Abuse Emergencies*. London: Academic Press.

Burr A. (1984). The illicit non-pharmaceutical heroin market and drug scene in Kensington Market. *Br. J. Addiction*; **September**: 337–43.

Castaneda C. (1970). *The Teachings of Don Juan*. London: Penguin.

Collins J., ed. (1982). *Drinking and Crime*. London: Tavistock Publications.

Cox T. R., Jacob M. R., LeBlanc A. E., eds. (1983). *Drugs and Drug Abuse: A Reference Text*. Toronto: ARF.

Department of Health and Social Security (1984). *Guidelines of Good Clinical Practice in the Treatment of Drug Abuse*. London: HMSO.

Edwards G., Arif A. (1980). *Drug Problems in the Sociocultural Context*. Geneva: World Health Organisation.

Edwards G. (1982). *The Treatment of Drinking Problems*. Oxford: Grant McIntyre.

Fordham M., ed. (1974). *Technique in Jungian Analysis*. London: William Heinemann.

Glatt M. (1982). *Alcoholism*. London: Hodder & Stoughton.

Haddon C. (1984). *Women and Tranquillisers*. London: Sheldon Press.

Hore B. D. (1976). *Alcohol Dependence*. Guildford: Butterworths.

Kalant O. J., ed. (1980). *Alcohol and Drug Problems in Women* (Volume 5 of Research Advances in Alcohol and Drug Problems). London: Plenum.

Kessel N., Walton H. (1982). *Alcoholism*. London: Penguin.

Laurie P. (1972). *Drugs*. London: Penguin.

Leech K. (1970). *A Practical Guide to the Drug Scene*. London: SPCK.

Leech K. (1983). *What Everyone Should Know About Drugs*. London: Sheldon Press.

Misuse of Drugs Act 1971. London: HMSO.

Report of Canadian Commission of Enquiry (1971). *The Non-Medical use of Drugs*. London: Penguin.

Richter D., ed. (1980). *Addiction and Brain Damage*. London: Plenum.

Ropp R. S. de (1958). *Drugs and the Mind*. London: Gollancz.

Smart C. (1984). Social policy and drug addiction. A critical study of policy development. *Br. J. Addiction*; **79**: 31–9.

Sourinhrin J., Baird J. A. (1984). The management of solvent misuse. A Glasgow community approach. *Br. J. Addiction*; **79**: 197–208.

Whitlock G. A. (1975). *Drugs, Morality and the Law*. Queensland: University of Queensland Press.

The Institute for the Study of Drug Dependence incorporates a library and information service. It also publishes helpful up-to-date pamphlets. Readers interested in further study are referred to the institute at: 1–4 Hatton Place, Hatton Garden, London EC1N 8ND; Tel: 01–430 1991.

Chapter 6
Mental Impairment

Most social workers will be familiar with mental handicap in their general practice. Thus it is not the purpose of this chapter to offer a comprehensive analysis of mental handicap or its place in society. However the 1983 Act includes within its scope the Mentally Handicapped person—whom it redefines as the Mentally Impaired person—and therefore some discussion of the social worker's role within the terms of the Act is important.

The 1983 Act refers to two categories of impairment: 'Severe Mental Impairment' and 'Mental Impairment'. It defines them thus:

' "severe mental impairment" means a state of arrested or incomplete development of mind which includes severe impairment of intelligence and social functioning and is associated with abnormally aggressive or seriously irresponsible conduct on the part of the person concerned.'

' "mental impairment" means a state of arrested or incomplete development of mind (not amounting to severe mental impairment) which includes significant impairment of intelligence and social functioning and is associated with *abnormally aggressive or seriously irresponsible conduct* on the part of the person concerned . . .'

Mental impairment is essentially an intellectual handicap which has existed since birth or an early age. Under other mental health legislation it has been known by different names, for example the 1959 Mental Health Act preferred 'mental subnormality' and legislation prior to that referred to the mental 'defective'.

Unlike previous legislation, the 1983 Act specifically does not allow mental impairment in itself to be the reason for compulsory hospitalisation: it must be linked to, or give rise to, aggressive or seriously irresponsible behaviour. Only then are there grounds for invoking a Compulsory Mental Health order. The difficulty facing approved social workers is that they are generally confronted with aggressive or irresponsible behaviour at the moment of a crisis, when a hospital admission may seem virtually inevitable. Has the mentally impaired person suddenly become unbearable? Or has something happened to precipitate behaviour that is out of the ordinary, dangerous or frightening?

Specialists in the field of mental impairment are now placing increasing importance on the role that the mentally impaired person is called on to play within their immediate social circle—be it family, community or hostel. This role could be such things as the 'eternal child', or the 'object of pity', or even the 'aggressive animal/vegetable'. Any changes, no matter how imperceptible, within the social circle, in expectation of the client with the impairment (for example parent suddenly falling ill) or in his treatment at the hands of others, can have dramatic and unforeseeable consequences on the client's behaviour.

Case illustration

This can be seen in the example of a 40-year-old client with a mental impairment causing him to have a mental age of seven. Intellectually, he will have the understanding of a child of seven years old. Emotionally and physically he will have the feelings and experience of a middle aged man. Clearly, it will be very hard for him to have insight into, and verbally express feelings about, his own and other people's motives. His reactions may therefore be quite extraordinary and hard for us to understand.

If, in addition to these internal difficulties, he has always been treated by his caring family in a particular way: for instance, overprotected as the 'eternal child', and given everything he wants, when he wants it, a social and behavioural problem will arise when eventually his family becomes exhausted and cannot cope by giving any more. The sudden introduction of their trying to say 'no' will be difficult for them to sustain, and the client to comprehend. All of a sudden 'everything' goes wrong, the client panics, becomes agitated and perhaps violent; the family feels guilty and retreats. The sudden retreat makes the client feel more insecure, provoking more disturbing behaviour in his panic-stricken search for a boundary. The situation spirals until the client becomes aggressive and uncontrollable. Over a period of years, he would appear to 'terrorise' his family. At the moment of crisis, his behaviour would indeed seem to be 'aggressive and seriously irresponsible'.

An initial move in a crisis, therefore, might be to give the client space to talk and express in words what it is that has provoked his behaviour. In this way, the focus can be shifted away from the client's impairment, and on to his feelings. Workers with experience of such crises will appreciate that this is not an easy attitude to adopt in the midst of violence, anguish or despair. It may not be possible. The situation may well be a very complex or desperate one, and hospital admission may be necessitated eventually in order to provide containment. But by careful negotiation, it may be possible to introduce some initial understanding which might enable the client to agree to go to hospital voluntarily. It may also sow the seeds of a trusting relationship to be continued throughout, and after, the crisis has been resolved.

Often, and especially in a crisis, the experience of the mentally impaired person is that he is not understood: strangers talk to his carer or complain *about* him, rather than *to* him. This can increase the feelings of isolation and stigma which may already exist within homes.

Where there have been no changes in the client's immediate social circle, nor reason for his aggressive or seriously irresponsible behaviour, then the possibility that he may be suffering from a mental illness will need to be considered. If he is, then the signs and symptoms of mental illness, as described in Chapter 1, will exist. This can make voluntary treatment more difficult to manage, and increase the likelihood that a compulsory admission to hospital will need to be made.

Treatment
Where assessment and diagnosis indicate that there is a psychiatric disorder accompanying mental impairment, behavioural techniques can be extremely valuable in helping the person and his family to cope with behaviour disturbances. Medication may be needed in order to treat the psychiatric disorder: this would be anti-psychotic or tranquillising, depending upon the diagnosis (see Chapter 9).

REFERENCES AND FURTHER READING

Anderson D. (1982). *Social Work and Mental Handicap*. London: Macmillan.

Balint M. (1964). *The Doctor, His Patient and the Illness*. London: Tavistock Publications.

Baumeister A., ed. (1968). *Mental Retardation: Appraisal, Education and Rehabilitation*. London: University of London Press.

Bayley M. (1973). *Mental Handicap and Community Care*. London: Routledge & Kegan Paul.

Clark A. D., Clark A. M. (1978). *Readings from Mental Deficiency*. London: Methuen.

Department of Health and Social Security (1980). *Mental Handicap: Progress, Problems and Priorities*. London: HMSO.

Department of Health and Social Security (1981). *Care in the Community*. London: HMSO.

Disability Rights Handbook. Compiled and published annually by The Disability Alliance, 25 Denmark Street, London W1. Tel: 01-240 0806.

Edgerton R. B. (1967). *The Cloak of Competence. Stigma in the Lives of the Mentally Retarded*. Berkeley: University of California Press.

Heaton-Ward W. A., Wiley Y. (1984). *Mental Handicap*. Bristol: John Wright.

Reid A. H. (1982). *The Psychiatry of Mental Handicap*. Oxford: Blackwell.

Ryan J., Thomas F. (1980). *The Politics of Mental Handicap*. London: Penguin.

Thompson T., Grabowski J., eds. (1972). *Behaviour Modification and the Mentally Retarded*. Oxford: Oxford University Press.

Wolfensberger W. (1972). *Normalisation*. London: National Institute of Mental Retardation.

Wolfensberger W. (1977). *A Multi-Component Advocacy Protection Scheme*. Toronto: Canadian Association for the Mentally Retarded.

Chapter 7
The Deaf Client

Deaf people are no more prone to mental illness than the hearing population (Denmark, 1983). They do, however, spend longer periods in hospital than hearing people because their communication problems interfere with diagnosis and treatment. Deaf patients can be misunderstood because they cannot articulate their needs and are, therefore, very vulnerable in a mental health situation. It was for this reason that the British Deaf Association asked Parliament to provide adequate provision in the 1983 Act to cover the special needs of deaf people.

Their proposal was adopted and included in Section 13 of the Act which requires approved social workers to interview *'in a suitable manner'*. This phrase is more fully explained in the DHSS Memorandum on the Act which spells out the meaning of the phrase *'taking into account any hearing or linguistic difficulties the patient may have'*. The following recommendations were made in the DHSS paper circulated to social services departments throughout the country and these can serve as useful guidelines for social workers working with the deaf mentally ill:

1. Wherever practicable those Specialist Social Workers with the Deaf employed by the Local Authority should be approved under the terms of the Mental Health Act 1983 and be called upon to interview a deaf person referred for possible admission to hospital. The British Deaf Association regards this as the preferable arrangement.
2. If (1) above is not practicable, the Specialist Social Worker with the Deaf should be called upon to act as a co-worker and to facilitate communication between the client and the approved social worker.
3. Where the local authority does not employ Specialist Social Workers with the Deaf, arrangements with neighbouring local authorities or local voluntary agencies should be established to provide either of the arrangements (1) and (2) above.
4. If efforts to obtain the services of a Specialist Social Worker with

the Deaf under the arrangements recommended ((1), (2) and (3) above) are unsuccessful, a record of the attempts made to do so should be kept.

5. Where it does not prove possible to involve the Specialist Social Worker with the Deaf at the point of referral, he/she should be involved as soon as possible afterwards as a co-worker.

6. In the training provided for potential approved social workers, information as to the local arrangements for access to Specialist Social Workers with the Deaf (within and outside office hours) should be made available.

Paragraph 276 of the DHSS Memorandum also draws attention to the need for appropriate methods of communication in conveying information to deaf patients:

'The nurse, doctor or other professional who explains the patient's rights to him should answer all reasonable questions, and should explain these matters to the patient in an appropriate way bearing in mind the patient's intelligence and any hearing disabilities or linguistic problems. For example, it should not be presumed that oral/aural and written methods will meet the needs of hearing impaired patients. In such cases the assistance of a Local Authority or voluntary agency Social Worker with the Deaf may be necessary.'

REFERENCES AND FURTHER READING

Denmark J. C. (1983). In *The Mental Health Act 1983 and the Deaf Patient*. London: The British Deaf Association.

Chapter 8
Cultural Factors

The approved social worker has a clear responsibility under the Mental Health Act to interview the client 'in a suitable manner', and also to consider 'all the circumstances of the case' (Section 13 (2) Mental Health Act 1983). In order to do this the approved social worker needs to be sensitive both to those cultural factors which influence the assessment of a situation, and also to the way behaviour is perceived by everyone involved. The demands of empathy, however, will take the social worker further: into an awareness of his own ethnic identity, an exploration of his own racialism and a consideration as to how this might impinge on the relationship between himself, the client and others involved in the assessment.

Social workers will be aware of the need not to stereotype anyone. This is particularly important when working with people from ethnic minorities. All black people are not Africans and ladies wearing saris may not be Indian! The experiences of different generations vary tremendously and this is particularly so in the case of ethnic minorities in this country.

IMMIGRANTS

To be an immigrant in a changed environment, to be subject to religious pressure or to be 'different' is stressful. The streets of an alien city can be very threatening. Immigrants often have to cope with the added stress of a challenge to their own sense of identity. They may have come to this country with certain expectations about how life is lived and how they will fit in. When they arrive, they face many surprises and may be left with experiences of shock, anger and confusion. In addition, they may find themselves inappropriately employed, in poor or overcrowded housing, or faced with discrimination which may, or may not be overt. Some may have to adapt to a very different climate, pace of living and perhaps a transition from rural to urban environment. Of course, many members of ethnic minority groups are not immigrants; they were born here and some are second and third generation with little direct experience of their country of origin. They may, however, have to cope with family expectations, religious pressures, alienation from their peers and a great deal of misunderstanding from members of the community. Stress induces fear, guilt, physical symptoms, jealousy, anger and aggression and people experiencing stress may need to control or deny this in very different ways.

The approved social worker has to start from a base of seeking to understand the meaning of the disturbed behaviour of a client and his attitude to those who are trying to help him. The personal history of all clients is important and in addition the social worker needs to recognise that stress is acted out in very many different ways, particularly where there is a cultural component. The social worker must try to understand what is 'normal' and what is 'abnormal' to the client and his family and to grasp the social reality of a particular system. It is too late for the social worker to wait actually to meet the situation at the point of crisis, he needs to equip himself beforehand. This means getting to know about ethnic minorities in his area and taking positive steps to discuss racialism.

There is no simple description of any cultural background, and stereotypes abound. There are, however, some very broad features which are helpful. Generally, those people who came to this country in the 1950s and 1960s as immigrants from India, Pakistan, Bangladesh, the Caribbean and other countries of the New Commonwealth are now permanently settled in this country. Their children may have been born here but will be influenced by the culture of their parents, which will differ in many ways from that of the indigenous population. The cultural patterns of the Indian sub-continent and the Caribbean are not at all alike and there are, within each culture, many variations. There is one cultural feature which they all share and that is that they have all, at some time in their history, been colonised. To a large extent colonial attitudes still exist in this country, on a conscious or unconscious level, and there are suppressed feelings of superiority of many white people and this has an effect on their perception of black people. The social worker must consider his own attitudes and those of other people, including the police, who may be involved either in the assessment of a crisis involving a mentally disordered person or in the provision of community support. Anyone who has worked in a psychiatric hospital will be aware that there is a high proportion not only of patients from ethnic minorities but also of staff from ethnic minorities. There are often social class differences between staff and patients and this can lead to misunderstandings or an unconscious need for distance between the disturbed person and the staff.

Immigrants from India

Approximately 80% of the people in India live in villages, although this is changing the majority of immigrants to this country from India will probably have come from a rural society. Family structure is predominantly that of the joint family, rather than the nuclear family, and married sons and their families as well as unmarried children usually live under the same roof as their parents. Households are often large and children may have many surrogate mothers. Individualism and self-determination are considered in Asian society to be less important than an individual's membership of, and obligation to, his family. Every family member has a distinct role to play and duties to perform. Authority lies with the elders who are responsible for decision making. Although many Asians share a similar cultural background there are distinct religious groups within Indian society. The three main faiths are Hinduism, Sikhism and Islam. Since the family as a group is more important than the individual in Asian society, relationships should not be considered in isolation but in terms of the whole family. Marriages are regarded as the union of families rather than of individuals and the family provides support for all its members, both physically and economically. Expected roles are clear to all members of the family. Property is often held in common and family resources pooled. The reputation of the family is important and the family ties are strong. The family is in many respects a community and intervention from outsiders may well be unacceptable or unsought. Very often it is more acceptable to present a physical symptom when stress is being experienced.

None of the three faiths of India consider women to be inferior but female roles are clearly defined. In Muslim society the system of purdah used to operate whereby women tried to avoid meeting men who were not related. This is particularly important to a male social worker or doctor and he should always consider the need to involve a female family member, or co-worker, if he feels that this might be an important factor in enabling a disturbed Muslim woman to feel able to talk about what is happening to her and express her feelings.

Immigrants from the Caribbean

The other main immigrant group is from the Caribbean. It is a mistake to presume that they all share a common culture as there are, in fact, many cultural differences within Caribbean people. The islands are thousands of miles apart (Jamaica, Trinidad, Barbados) as well as mainland Guyana and Belize, and have different religions and social atmospheres. The majority, however, are descendants of people who were slaves and whose original culture was modified by the situation they were forced into. People were removed from the traditional tribal life of Africa and taken to a life of slavery where several different Western European nations exercised direct control over them. The family structure was broken down and customs destroyed. Parents and children were often split up and sent to different areas, indeed the breakdown of families was often a matter of policy. They were not allowed to marry and fathers had no rights or duties towards their children. At the same time they were forced to adapt to Western European cultures and religions, particularly the Evangelical forms of Christianity.

It is impossible to describe a 'typical' West Indian family but in many homes the women may tend to play the dominant role and the grandmother is often the effective family head. Children may be mothered by unmarried women in an accepting family environment in which the men may be absent. They cannot automatically call on relatives for support and rigid roles and obligations towards family members may not exist. The amount of help received from each other depends on personal relationships rather than upon duty.

SPECIAL RISK GROUPS

Within ethnic minority groups there is some evidence that certain members have been found to be at special risk psychiatrically. These include adolescents and Muslim women. As all social workers know, adolescence is a normal period of turmoil and growth. However, children born of immigrant parents have added difficulties when they reach adolescence. They may find themselves caught between two cultures and feel that they belong to none. Many such adolescents are unable to identify with their white peers or with their own families. In the case of Asian girls they may be faced with an expectation of an arranged marriage and this may lead them to run away from home or contemplate suicide. Many young black people find themselves living through the conflict of adolescence in a setting of misunderstanding, unequal opportunity and feeling of hostility towards the society in which they live.

The problems of Muslim women are often concerned with isolation. They may be required to remain at home and not encouraged to leave the house. Their husbands often work long hours and these women can become totally isolated, unable to speak English and consequently may suffer from acute depression. Hindu and Sikh women may face some of the problems experienced by Muslim women but they are usually able to go out to work. They are, however, sometimes expected to do all the work of the house with no help from other members of the family. They also have to offer hospitality to many visitors. It is easy to see why they become physically worn out and very vulnerable. Their husbands may at the same time be experiencing prejudice and discrimination, along with adjusting to a new culture and feel devalued and without the support of the extended family. For example, if the social worker is called to help a young married Asian woman who never leaves the house but sits gazing at the wall, then what is happening to her has a distinct significance if she comes from a Muslim background in which it is normal for women seldom to go out alone and where she now finds herself in a new country where the only person she knows is her husband. She is deprived of family supports and feels lonely, isolated and probably very frightened. Her husband may be working very long hours to send money back home to both of their families for whom he feels he has a responsibility. In such a situation the young woman may well find it extremely difficult to talk to a male social worker and it is absolutely imperative that someone from her own culture is involved in helping the social worker make the assessment and in explaining to the woman and her husband exactly where there is cause for concern.

The British Association for Social Work (BASW) has issued guidelines for preparation and practice for social work in multi-cultural Britain. This is obtainable from BASW, and contains the addresses of many of the key organisations involved with ethnic minorities.

THE USE OF INTERPRETERS

The approved social worker has a responsibility to interview the client in a 'suitable manner'. Obviously, where there is likely to be a language difficulty the social worker needs to involve a translator. Trust needs to be developed between the translator and the social worker and where there are a large number in an area who have a different language, e.g. Polish or Chinese, the approved social worker should know translators and help them to understand what is involved in translating during an assessment of a mentally ill person. It is important to remember that even where the client seems to understand English there may actually be language or conceptional difficulties, e.g. the client may have words for concrete matters but not for feelings or concepts. When he is under stress this may easily lead to his problem being misunderstood or for his behaviour to be seen as more disordered than it really is. The use of an interpreter is not merely that of finding someone who knows the language; it needs to be someone who also knows the social worker, the agency, and understands something about the situation.

Interpreting by a child should be regarded as unethical and unprofessional and certainly should not be contemplated in any other way than the most superficial level. The interpreter needs to be familiar with the basic principles of the social worker such as impartiality, confidentiality, the use of silence, the legal framework and also should not be afraid of being with mentally ill people. This is asking a great deal of the interpreter and the social worker has to be prepared to put in quite a lot of time and effort in order to select and support interpreters. The 1983 Mental Health Act has particularly placed the duty on the social worker to interview in a 'suitable manner' and a client would have a right to complain to a tribunal if he felt that he had not understood what was happening or if he could not make himself understood to the doctors and social worker.

It is important to emphasise that an understanding of cultural factors should be an *ongoing* commitment of the approved social worker. It has become a truism to say that we live in a time when the only constancy is change. Yet this puts an increased demand on us as social workers. Fundamental to any work with people from ethnic minorities is a sensitivity to the additional stress they experience both from within their own culture and from the rest of the community and also the very real danger that their response to stress may be interpreted as some sort of psychotic breakdown. Stress can induce fear, guilt, physical symptoms, jealousy, anger and regression. Paranoid feelings are common and often have a reality base, either in the present or early experiences of the client. People under stress may need to control it in very different ways and when trying to help a client from a different culture the social worker must pay a great deal of attention to clarifying with the client and the family exactly who he is and why he has been asked to intervene. The social worker should not assume that the client knows who has sent him or even understands what a 'social services department' is. It is often difficult for clients to understand who has 'sent' the social worker to see them and they may fear that they are being secretly investigated by the police, the Home Office or the authorities.

The social worker needs to avoid the use of jargon and to be quite sure that he is communicating what he means and that he is being understood. There can be a literal response to questions such as 'Can you hear voices?'. Sometimes stress may be dealt with by an exaggerated use of religious ritual such as trance or hysteria and the social worker needs to distinguish between what is normal or abnormal, in both a personal and cultural sense.

In conclusion, understanding the problem of ethnic minorities can only be done by social workers who have a grasp of the social reality of their clients and make every effort to listen to and share something of the experiences of ethnic minority clients. If we accept 'all behaviour has meaning', then it is imperative that whatever is being presented is seen not only from a medical/psychological perspective but also in a social family context. We should all make efforts to be aware of the cultural factors which affect ethnic minority groups living in our communities and also try to discover our own racialism. This is particularly important to social workers, doctors, nurses, teachers and anyone working with mentally ill people where, of course, communication skills and sensitivity to stress are essential. The approved social worker will wish to make efforts to be in touch with local ethnic organisations and community relations workers. He will be aware that a basic understanding of the social systems, religious beliefs and attitudes of clients is equally as important to his practice as is a clinical knowledge of psychiatry.

REFERENCES AND FURTHER READING

Bierer J., Burke A. W. (1984). Transcultural psychiatry: racism and mental illness. *Int. J. Social Psychiatry*; 3(1/2).

Biko S. (1979). *I Write What I Like*. London: William Heinemann.

Cleave E. (1968). *Soul on Ice*. Toronto: Dell Publishing.

Daniel W. W. (1970). *Racial Discrimination in England*. London: Penguin.

Field G., Haikin P. (1971). *Black Britons*. Oxford: Oxford University Press.

Foulkes E. F., Wintrob R. M., Westermeyer J., Cavazza A. R. (1977). *Current Perspectives in Cultural Psychiatry*. Englewood Cliffs, NJ: Spectrum.

GLC Women's Committee Bulletin (1984). *London Against Racism Issue*; 13(Jan/Feb).

Henley A. (1979). *Asian Patients in Hospital and at Home*. London: King Edward's Hospital Fund.

Jung C. G. (1974). Civilization in transition. In *Collected Works, Volume 10*. London: Routledge & Kegan Paul.

Kiev A. (1972). *Transcultural Psychiatry*. New York: Free Press.

Leff J. (1981). *Psychiatry Around the Globe*. New York: Dekker.

Lipsedge M., Littlewood R. (1983). *Aliens and Alienists*. London: Penguin.

Watson J. L. (1977). *Between Two Cultures*. Oxford: Blackwell.

Chapter 9
Methods of Treatment

INTRODUCTION

The treatment of the mentally ill has a long and often controversial history. In this introduction we want to concentrate on an outline of the developments that have occurred since the early fifties with the advent of the neuroleptic drugs which made possible the social changes within and outside the mental hospital. These were subsequently consolidated in the Mental Health Acts (1959) and (1983).

Neuroleptic drugs

One of the most significant advances during this period was the introduction of the neuroleptic drugs. Until the early fifties such drugs that were available in psychiatry did not produce a tranquillising effect on the patient's disturbed behaviour but usually put him to sleep. For the first time drugs could now be used to calm the mind rather than sedate and induce sleep. This was a big step forward, for it enabled patients to become more accessible. Their inner turmoil, often caused by delusions and hallucinations, was reduced and this helped many patients to become more in touch with themselves and their environment.

Table 9.1   Models of mental illness: historical development

Diagnosis	Treatment
Possession	Exorcism
Sin	Persecution
Madness	Asylum
Illness	Medical treatment
Illness/ social dysfunction	Medical treatment/ community care

The importance of this cannot be overstated, for before such drugs were introduced mental hospitals were extremely disturbed places which often prevented any helpful interaction from taking place between staff and patients. The rigid routine on most wards was focussed on controlling and containing patients who were either in wild states of excitement or withdrawn and stupored. After taking neuroleptic drugs most patients became less troubled by their illness and the general atmosphere on the wards became less chaotic and more relaxed. This allowed for more therapeutic relationships to take place between patients and staff. Hitherto most mental hospitals had largely been custodial and repressive institutions which produced many of the secondary handicaps of mental illness. These disabilities were largely caused by the process which came to be known as 'Institutionalisation'. (These disabilities were originally described by Dr D. V. Martin and Dr Russell Barton.)

Such closed institutions denied patients their individuality and responsibility for themselves. They became apathetic, unable to make choices and decisions about their lives and became totally dependent on the hospital to meet all their needs. It would perhaps be unfair to say that all patients suffered from such a regime. Many must have benefited from the sense of sanctuary and asylum that some of these hospitals offered.

The therapeutic community

About the same time that the new drugs were being widely used in the treatment of mental disorder other changes were taking place. Dr Maxwell Jones and his team at Belmont Hospital (now the Henderson Hospital) were working with the new concept of the therapeutic community. Here a more democratic approach in psychiatric care was being made. Authority and responsibility were shared between the clinical team and patients in the various therapeutic group activities. Everyone participated in the decision-making process within the community and this helped patients to begin to take responsibility for themselves and each other.

It created situations in which patients could examine their motives and behaviour so that a better understanding of each other's problems could be made. The community enabled open communication in small groups, community meetings as well as the daily round to share and work through the problems patients encountered in relationships with each other. This revolutionary idea was subsequently developed within the community and influenced and altered the traditional hierarchical approach of many mental hospitals.

Over the next two decades we began to see a shift in psychiatric care away from the large mental hospitals to the psychiatric units attached to district general hospitals. The more capable patients were discharged and resettled in the community. Many patients were discharged to community care which, sadly, was largely ill-prepared for the new demands. Although provisions were uneven throughout the country innovations were made and are now common practice. These include community psychiatric nurses, hostels, day centres, group homes and adult fostering schemes.

Therapeutic intervention and social change

A helpful model, which demonstrates a relationship between therapeutic activity (including social work) and social change has been developed by Sue Holland (1984) and is illustrated in Fig. 9.1:

RADICAL CHANGE

	Radical humanism DESIRE	Radical structuralism ACTION	
SUBJECTIVE			OBJECTIVE
	MEANING Interpretative	SYMPTOM Functionalism	

REGULATION

Fig. 9.1 Adapted from Burrell and Morgan (1979), reproduced with permission of Sue Holland.

'The horizontal dimension runs between the objective and subjective poles. *Objectivism* emphasises a natural science model; the organism, or even the machine. Things are measured and quantified. The other polar extreme is *subjectivism* which emphasises the unique qualities of human experience, interpretation of meanings and use of symbols. The vertical dimension at one end suggests a relatively static or slowly evolving social situation and at the other one in which radical change is an inevitable, even desirable state.'

METHODS OF TREATMENT IN PSYCHIATRY

These can be divided into three main approaches:

1. Physical treatment:
    (a) Chemotherapy (medication).
    (b) Electro-convulsive therapy (ECT).

    (c) Psychosurgery (leucotomy).

    (d) Hormonal implant.

2. Psychotherapy:

    (a) Individual.

    (b) Group.

    (c) Marital and family therapy.

    (d) Behaviour therapy.

3. Rehabilitation: this is discussed more fully in Chapter 11.

PHYSICAL TREATMENT

Physical treatments in psychiatry have come and gone but some have remained and stood the test of time. Electro-convulsive therapy remains the standard treatment for severe endogenous depression and psychosurgery is still used in very rare clinical situations.

CHEMOTHERAPY

The development of the neuroleptic and antidepressant medication has done much to reduce the distress associated with psychiatric illness, particularly in those suffering from psychoses. In many cases it has led to patients being in hospital for shorter periods of time, with others it has prevented the need for admission. Chemotherapy is the generic term to describe treatment given in the form of medication. Most of the drugs used in psychiatry affect the mood and are called psychotropic. This speciality is now called psychopharmacology.

The use of drugs in psychiatry dates back to earliest times, for instance opium, morphine and cocaine. Resperpine, a drug used to lower blood pressure and calm disturbance has been used in India for over three thousand years. This drug was used in Western psychiatry in the fifties but has now been replaced by the more refined neuroleptic drugs.

The following classification of medication is used in general psychiatry:

1. Major tranquillisers (neuroleptics):

    (a) Phenothiazines.

    (b) Butyrophenones.

2. Minor tranquillisers (anxiolytics).

3. Sedatives/hypnotics.

4. Antidepressants.

Major tranquillisers (neuroleptics)

These form the major tranquillisers and are used in the treatment of schizophrenia, hypomania and other mental disorders. Neuroleptic drugs have now been used for over thirty years; they have stood the test of time in treating the severe disruptions and disorganised aspects of psychotic behaviour such as gross excitement, agitation and aggression.

Phenothiazines

Phenothiazines is the sub-group which includes the standard drugs like Largactil and Stelazine. These have an anti-psychotic effect in the sense that they calm the patient and reduce much of the distress caused by the active symptoms of delusions and auditory hallucinations. Psychiatrists question whether these drugs reverse the psychotic process or whether they simply act by suppressing the psychotic symptoms.

All of these drugs seem to be effective in diminishing the emotional response to both the internal and external stimuli. Since the phenothiazine drugs were first discovered in the early fifties other types have been developed from the same chemical family and include Melliril, Fentazin and Sparine. It is often a matter of clinical judgement which particular drugs are used.

Butyrophenones

These drugs are more potent than the above tranquillisers and are primarily used in the treatment of dopamine receptors in the brain which produce a slowing down of psycho-motor activity. Haloperidol is the most popular drug used in this group. This drug is slowly excreted from the body and its accumulative effect can soon produce toxicity. It is therefore usually given in smaller doses to reduce the risk of toxic effects. The side-effects from this group tend to be greater than those found in phenothiazines.

Minor tranquillisers (anxiolytics)

These are the minor tranquillisers and because they have received much publicity because of their abuse, they are household names. They include drugs like Valium and Librium which, used carefully, are effective in reducing much of the distress associated with psychoneuroses and in the treatment of the withdrawal symptoms of alcoholism. Unlike the major tranquillisers, the side-effects from this group of drugs are minimal. However, there is growing evidence that many people become dependent on these drugs and if withdrawn

Table 9.2 Medication used in the treatment of neuroses

Proprietary name	Official name	Usual dose	Side-effects	Remarks
Librium	Chlordiazepoxide	10–60 mg daily	Drowsiness	All drugs of benzodiazepine type reduce the patient's tolerance for alcohol
				The ability to drive, operate machinery, etc. may be reduced
Valium	Diazepam	2–40 mg daily	Drowsiness	Possibility of dependence on and tolerance to these drugs
Ativan	Lorazepam	0.5–4 mg daily	Drowsiness	
Mogadon	Nitrazepam	5–10 mg before retiring		Used for insomnia associated with anxiety
Melleril	Thioridazine	25–300 mg daily		
Inderal	Propranolol	20–80 mg daily	Hypotension	Possibility of convulsions when high doses are stopped suddenly

Table 9.3   Medication used in the treatment of mania

Proprietory name	Official name	Usual dose	Side-effects	Remarks
Serenace	Haloperidol	5–100 mg daily	Lowers blood pressure	
Largactil	Chlorpromazine		See Table 9.4	
Priadel Camcolit	Lithium carbonate	600–1200 mg daily	Gastro intestinal upsets Thirst Excessive urination Tremor Hypothyroidism	Very careful monitoring of blood levels. Also tests of renal and thyroid functions. Dangerous in overdose. Takes six/twelve months to be effective

suddenly they do suffer from a withdrawal syndrome which can include symptoms of sleeplessness, acute panic and depression.

It should be stressed that all drugs listed potentiate effects with alcohol.

Sedatives/hypnotics

As their names suggest, these drugs sedate and are primarily used in the treatment of insomnia to help induce sleep. Sleep disturbance is a common symptom of many psychiatric conditions, particularly depression, mania, schizophrenia, and other disorders where there is a marked increase in anxiety.

Barbiturates were the most common group of sedatives until it was found that they had an addictive effect. They were abused and proved fatal in overdose. These drugs have now been replaced in favour of the safer and less addictive benzodiazepine group which includes sleeping tablets such as Mogadon and Dalmane.

Hypnotic drugs are useful in helping to induce sleep, but do not affect the underlying cause of sleep disturbance.

Antidepressant medication

Drugs used in the treatment of depression can be divided into two main groups:

1. The tricyclics.
2. The monoamine oxidase inhibitors (MAOIs).

Before the above drugs were introduced to treat depression, amphetamines or the so called 'pep pills' were commonly used in the treatment of clinical depression. These drugs produced rapid dependence and doses had to be increased to create the desired effect. Although they temporarily lifted the patient's mood they did not alter the basic cause of the depressive illness. The person was often left feeling flat, empty and more depressed. In large doses amphetamines often produced paranoid psychosis and patients sometimes experienced terrifying persecution in the form of visual hallucinations, often referred to as 'the horrors'. These drugs have now been withdrawn from the clinical treatment of depression, and have been replaced by the following groups.

Tricyclics
Antidepressant medication has made a major breakthrough in the treatment of depression. Unlike the neuroleptics and sedatives, the

Table 9.4 Medication used in the treatment of schizophrenia

Proprietary name	Official name	Usual dose	Side-effects	Remarks
Largactil	Chlorpromazine	100–1000 mg daily orally or intramuscular injection	Drowsiness Sensitivity to sunlight Jaundice Parkinsonian symptoms Mask like face, tremors Stiff limbs	Stop or reduce dose Use anti-Parkinsonian drugs as appropriate
Stelazine Orap	Trifluperazine Pimozide	1–20 mg daily 1–12 mg daily		
Long-acting injections				
Modecate	Fluphenazine	40–200 mg every two weeks	Tardive dyskinesia	May persist or worsen if drug is stopped
Depixol Clopixol	Flupenthixol Clopenthixol	100–400 mg every two weeks		May precipitate convulsions

Table 9.5 Medication used in the treatment of depression

Proprietary name	Official name	Usual dose	Side-effects	Remarks
Tofranil	Imipramine	50–200 mg daily	Energising; useful if retardation is marked	Dangerous, particularly heart complications if overdosed
	Amitriptyline	50–200 mg daily	Can precipitate mania	No effect for 10–14 days
	Dothiepin	50–200 mg daily	Dry mouth Constipation	
	Mianserin	30–120 mg daily		Safer in overdose
	Phenelzine	45–60 mg daily		Needs special diet: no broad beans, cheese or marmite
Optimax	Tryptophan			Efficacy less established than others

tricyclics do not affect the mood right away. The improvement is usually felt by the patient between 7 and 21 days after the treatment has commenced. These drugs must therefore be taken for the full period before one can be certain they are going to work.

Studies have shown that this group of drugs is the safest and most effective antidepressant medication. About 2/3 of depressed patients respond and improve on them. Patients who do best are those who suffer from a clear-cut depressive illness with restlessness and anxiety. Because these drugs contain a compound with a pronounced sedative effect (chemically they are related to the neuroleptics), a dose can often be taken at night to help produce a good night's sleep.

Antidepressant medication has considerably reduced the need for ECT. When ECT is used and tricyclics are given simultaneously they can often reduce the number of ECT treatments required. It is interesting to note that this kind of medication has no effect in elevating mood in 'normal people'. It is only effective where there is a depressive mood disorder. In other words, it does not act as an euphoriant like amphetamine, which has a more direct stimulating effect on the central nervous system.

The monoamine oxidase inhibitors (MAOIs)

Many clinical trials have shown that this type of medication is not as effective as the above group in depressive illness. In addition, there are serious side-effects if certain types of cheese, yeast, or other foodstuffs are eaten. These drugs are usually reserved for patients with so called atypical depression, and those who have failed to respond to other antidepressant medications. MAOIs have been used with some success in the treatment of phobic disorders.

Lithium carbonate

Lithium carbonate is a simple substance which is now used with success in the short and long-term treatment of affective disorders. It has also been shown to prevent or substantially reduce manic and depressive episodes where there is a recurrence of these mood swings. Patients who seem to benefit most are those who have suffered a manic depressive illness and who have had about three episodes during the previous five years.

Three main factors are crucial when considering giving such treatment:

1. The severity of the affective disorder.
2. The wishes of the patient.
3. The patient's reliability in taking regular medication.

The third point is very important for patients must attend regularly for blood tests. A high degree of cooperation is necessary for the treatment to be effective.

Because affective disorder seems to be a life-long illness treatment must be planned accordingly. Lithium carbonate would seem to be the most appropriate way of managing the illness once the confidence of the patient has been established.

Side-effects of neuroleptic drugs

The phenothiazine group of drugs has become the standard medication treatment for schizophrenia. It is also used in other major psychotic disorders and has brought considerable relief to the sufferers. These drugs do however, produce unwanted side-effects and these can be listed under four groups.

All these side effects are known as extrapyramidal symptoms.

Pseudo Parkinsonism

This mimics some of the signs and symptoms of Parkinson's disease. The patient develops a mask-like facial expression, tremor of hands and general stiffening of the limbs.

Akathisia

This condition is marked by restlessness where the patient is unable to keep still, fidgets, tends to shuffle and rocks his body backwards and forwards.

Acute dyskinesias

These are more acute reactions. Oculogyric crisis is the most common. It starts with a fixed stare, then the eyes turn upwards and this is followed by great tension in the neck and opening of the mouth. This is a most alarming sight and it can last a few hours before subsiding spontaneously.

Other dyskinesic reactions can include the trunk and limbs, producing grotesque postures or writhing movements. All these reactions are extremely distressing both to the patient and the onlooker.

Chronic tardive dyskinesia

This is characterised by continuous chewing movements involving head and tongue and certain postural changes. These can persist even when the neuroleptic medication has been stopped.

The patient may also complain of dry mouth, blurred vision and weight gain. The latter symptom may be the result of the fact that phenothiazine can stimulate the appetite.

Side-effects of antidepressant medication

Like other drug groups antidepressant medication can also produce unwanted side-effects although in the case of tricyclics they are less severe.

Tricyclics

Hypotension (reduced blood pressure), dryness of the mouth, sweating, constipation, urinary delay, blurred vision and in very rare cases patients can become hypomanic. This latter effect is usually found in patients who are prone to recurrent mood disorders.

MOAIs

The most serious side-effects are hepatotoxicity and interaction with food and other drugs (like pethidine). Sudden severe and intense headaches can be experienced as a result of these drugs' interaction with such foods as cheese, broad beans, marmite and beef extracts.

Other side-effects include elation, sexual impotence, failure of orgasm, blurred vision, dryness of mouth and constipation. Clearly because of these complications, patients taking MOAIs need to be under careful medical supervision.

Depot injections

There are many patients who need to take medication on a regular basis, over long periods of time, while others may need to take it for the rest of their lives. Depot injections are long acting, slow releasing neuroleptic drugs which are given at regular intervals, usually between two to four weeks, the particular dose will depend on individual needs. This method of administering medication has been shown to be more reliable and effective than oral medication.

Some patients stop taking medication for a number of reasons, perhaps prominent amongst these are because the person feels better and no longer feels the need to continue taking tablets. Others may find the side-effects too distressing and then fail to persevere with them. With others it may be due to their illness; they may be too confused, lacking in sight or just forget to take them. This is the most frequent cause of relapse and need for readmission to hospital in schizophrenia.

Treatment of schizophrenia is a complex interaction between medication and the psycho-social factors in the patient's life. For example it has been shown that neuroleptics protect the schizophrenic from life stresses and considerably reduce the risk of relapse.

Depot injections come in various makes. Depixol Modecate is the commonest in use. These injections are given intramuscularly in the patient's buttock. This produces a store of the drug in the body and by drawing on this store gradually a sustained level of the drug in the blood and brain is able to extend control over symptoms for periods of two to four weeks. These injections are usually given to the patient at home or in special out-patient clinics by a community psychiatric nurse. The regular contact between nurse and patient also offers the opportunity to monitor the patient's general progress.

ELECTRO-CONVULSIVE THERAPY (ECT)

A knowledge of the historical developments and mode of action of ECT treatment is given here in the hope that this will give workers a better understanding of this often controversial form of treatment. It is hoped that this will dispel some fantasies and enable social workers to explain to clients and their families the mode of action of ECT and some of its implications.

In the 1920s it was observed that some epileptics who also suffered from schizophrenia seemed to improve following a seizure. Often the disorder of thought and mood would temporarily clear. This prompted some workers to postulate that schizophrenia and epilepsy were biologically antagonistic. (This later proved to be a mistaken belief.) Such a view encouraged others to experiment with ways of artificially inducing epileptic fits in schizophrenics.

Meduna, in 1933, began testing the ability of chemical substances like camphor and, later, cardizol to produce seizures. Patients using these substances showed some improvement. However, this method was extremely crude and the fits produced were uncontrolled and difficult to terminate, which made such treatment hazardous.

It was not until Cerlette and Bini in 1938 introduced an electrical method of inducing convulsions that a more universal interest grew. This method used bitemporal electrodes which passed an electrical current through the brain, rendering the patient unconscious and producing a grand mal fit. This technique enabled the doctor for the first time to have a greater control over the duration and extent of the seizure. The most dangerous complications resulting from this method were fractures and dislocations of bones which were the result of the violence of the fit.

Electro-convulsive therapy was first introduced into the UK in 1940. An important modification was made in 1941 when curare was introduced to paralyse the muscles of the patient during treatment. This was given without a general anaesthetic but did reduce the above complications. In the 1950s short-acting anaesthesia were given with muscle relaxants. The patient became unconscious and this prevented him from experiencing the frightening respiratory paralysis and the general fear associated with the treatment. Anaesthesia was only given in sufficient quantity to ensure an adequate convulsion (i.e. a grand mal epileptic fit). It was the quality of the fit which appeared crucial to the effectiveness of ECT.

From its crude origins ECT was becoming more humane and sophisticated and, with the help of a competent anaesthetist, this made it a remarkably safe treatment. Such technical advances were not, however, matched by an understanding of how the treatment worked, and many remain in opposition to its use. Epileptic seizures have always been the subject of fear and stigma by the general public. To induce artificially such seizures seems to many to be denigrating and brutal to the individual.

Since the introduction of antidepressant medication ECT has been substantially reduced. It is now sparingly used, often only in those cases where medication has failed to bring relief and only for specific disorders. These can be summarised as the severely depressed disorders, like endogenous depression, where the patient is suffering from mental retardation, nihilistic delusions, agitation, life-threatening weight loss and strong suicidal thoughts. Some authorities also believe it to be of benefit in mania, acute schizophrenia and in puerperal psychoses.

Electro-convulsive therapy is customarily given two or three times a week. Since memory disturbance has been minimised it can now be given more frequently, though this is seldom done. Many respond well to five treatments but others require more. If improvement does not occur after seven convulsions it is rarely advisable to continue.

The question of brain damage as a result of ECT remains debatable. There is clearly interference with brain functioning as shown by confusion and memory disturbances. There is, however, no evidence to suggest that structural brain damage occurs. The memory disturbance following treatment soon clears. Objective tests have shown that memory disturbance completely disappears after one month.

It might be helpful if we look at the step-by-step medical procedure adopted for the administration of ECT so that social workers will then be in a better position to explain to their clients what actually takes place.

Mode of treatment

Before ECT is administered a thorough medical examination is made to ensure the patient is fit enough to undergo the treatment. This is normal procedure when a general anaesthetic is involved. Although ECT can be given on an out-patient basis, it is better done on an in- patient basis so that observation may be made before and following treatment.

Treatment is usually conveniently given in the morning, when the patient should not eat or drink anything. Half an hour before treatment is given, an injection of premedication of Atropine and a tranquilliser is administered. This helps prevent salivation and vomiting and the tranquilliser will allay any anxiety. Before the ECT treatment is given the patient is seen by the anaesthetist who administers an intravenous injection of short-acting anaesia (thiopentone) and a muscle relaxant. The psychiatrist places the unilateral electrodes either side of the patient's head and a fit is then induced by the passage of an electrical current.

The convulsion usually occurs immediately and lasts about 30–40 seconds. The patient is given oxygen by the anaesthetist until spontaneous respiration is re-established. He is then laid on his side until he regains consciousness which varies between 5 and 15 minutes. He may on recovery be confused and suffer memory disturbance. This is a temporary phase, however, and passes after a short period of time.

The mechanism of its action is not yet fully understood, indeed it remains a mystery. The improvement in the patient's mood is not so related to the amount of electric current passed as to the extent of the fit that is induced. Electro-convulsive therapy is given in a course of about 6–12 sessions but this is largely determined by the result of each treatment.

POTENTIALLY IRREVERSIBLE TREATMENT

This is dealt with under the Act in Section 57 (Part IV). It is generally taken to include psychosurgery and hormone implant treatment. In view of their potentially irreversible and controversial nature such treatments are given only where the patient consents, *and* a second, independent medical opinion agrees. Two other opinions must also be sought from two non-medical persons who have been involved in the patient's treatment – for example, his social worker.

Due to the serious nature of such treatment, these procedures must be applied whether the patient is of a formal or informal status. Under Section 60, the patient may withdraw his consent, and treatment terminate, at any time.

PSYCHOSURGERY (LEUCOTOMY)

Egas Moniz, a Portuguese surgeon, developed the first leucotomy operation in 1936; and this became the standard practice until the 1950s when it fell into disrepute because of the high number of side-effects. The operation (which literally means cutting of the white matter) consisted of drilling two burr holes, one on each side of the frontal part of the skull. A knife known as the leucotome was then used to sever and divide the white fibre tracts between the frontal lobes and hypothalamus parts of the brain. This pathway is responsible for the regulation of emotional responses and tension.

The pre-frontal leucotomy was performed on an enormous number of patients with a wide range of mental disorders. The early claims that it could cure symptoms of schizophrenia and chronic depression soon lost ground, for many of these patients developed side-effects which were worse than the original disorder. They included an increase in apathy, inertia, loss of initiative and drive. Many were reduced to vegetable-like existence with flat emotional response, loss of judgement and deterioration of social behaviour. Others developed epilepsy and became incontinent.

In the 1960s the operation was modified (bimedial or rostral) and seemed to have a lower incidence of side-effects and complications. In the 1970s the operation underwent further developments and the stereotactic leucotomy was introduced. Here small areas of the brain could be destroyed with great accuracy and on a specific site and again claims were made that it had further reduced side-effects.

Those who are referred for psychosurgery must have been treated extensively with all other forms of treatment without effect. The main disorders which seem to benefit are the following:

1. Long standing obsessional states.
2. Chronic depression.
3. Aggression.
4. Certain schizophrenic conditions.
5. Intractable severe pain.

Because of the controversy of this form of treatment and its irreversible effects it is dealt with under the Consent to Treatment Provisions Category in Part IV of the 1983 Act. (See Part II of the present text for legal requirements.)

HORMONAL IMPLANT TREATMENT

Hormone implant is used primarily in the treatment of sexual offenders when efforts to administer the hormones by mouth have proven to be unreliable. The effect of the treatment is to reduce the libido of the male to the point of impotence.

Since 1963 this treatment has been carried out on sexual offenders where the criteria consist of the subjective certainty of reconviction if no help is given, that the individual's history suggests reconviction, and that the IQ is too low, or there is limited capacity to verbalise difficulties, making the person unsuitable for psychotherapy.

Hormone implant treatment is carried out mainly in prison settings, where in most cases the prisoner is serving a sentence for sexual assault on children. Due to the highly controversial nature of this treatment the Act provides stringent safeguards to protect patients' and prisoners' rights.

PSYCHOTHERAPY

Psychotherapy may be broadly defined as any psychological treatment which uses verbal communication to understand and influence the patient's attitudes and behaviour. Using this definition, psychotherapy is practised by many social workers in varying degrees of intensity, ranging from brief and irregular contact to more regular formally structured hourly sessions taking place over a period of time.

Psychotherapy can be divided into the following types:

1. Individual psychotherapy:
   (a) Supportive.
   (b) Intensive.
   (c) Psychoanalysis.
2. Group psychotherapy.
3. Marital and family therapy.
4. Behaviour therapy.

INDIVIDUAL PSYCHOTHERAPY

Supportive

This is perhaps the commonest type used in psychiatry. It entails the following techniques which have much in common with the social casework process.

1. Ventilation. This offers the patient the opportunity to ventilate his problems both in the 'here and now' and those which have occurred in the past.

2. Clarification. Here problems are discussed and the therapist discusses their nature and how they may be affecting the patient's present behaviour.
3. Abreaction. This process enables the patient to express highly charged emotions within the safety of the therapeutic relationship. This usually includes feelings of rage, resentment, anxiety and grief.
4. Suppression. The therapist is more authoritarian in this role and often uses a more directive approach, i.e. he gives advice, uses persuasion and suggestion.

Intensive

This method is more structured and entails greater skills of the unconscious processes. The main body of theory is based on Freudian psychoanalytical work and uses the central concept of transference to help understand unconscious motivation. This therapy is practiced by qualified psychotherapists who, in addition to having a basic qualification such as social work, medicine and psychology, will have taken a psychotherapy course which as part of their training includes their own personal analysis. This helps the therapist to deal with problems in his own make up so they do not harmfully interfere with the objectivity and effectiveness of the therapeutic relationship. In contrast to supportive psychotherapy, the patient is usually seen on a regular basis, for an hour one or more times per week over an extended period of time. The therapist takes a more objective role using the phenomenon known as transference. Here the patient transfers emotions he has towards important figures from his childhood, namely his mother and father. During the treatment, he re-experiences these feelings and conflicts which may have shaped his present difficulties.

The analysis of the transference relationship is the crucial way of understanding and reconstructing the patient's unconscious neurosis so that it can be dealt with and worked through in the relationship with the therapist. It is the constant repetition of these early patterns of experience and the subsequent interpretation of them that eventually brings conviction, insight and change in the patient's way of dealing with his problems. Most patients who are referred for this type of therapy are suffering from psychoneurotic disorders, psychosomatic disorders and those suffering from personality difficulties which prevent them from making satisfactory relationships. This form of psychotherapy is not generally regarded as being suitable for psychotic conditions.

Clearly such treatment is time consuming and costly and because of this it is not always available on the National Health Service. Much will depend on the psychotherapeutic services in a particular area; the severity of the disorder and whether alternative methods of treatment are available. Intensive psychotherapy requires considerable cooperation in terms of time and effort and those who are referred for this type of therapy must fulfil fairly rigorous criteria. They need, for example, to be well motivated, have the ability to verbalise, have the necessary ego strength to bear the pain of insight and change.

Because psychotherapy is not readily available on the NHS, many psychotherapists practise privately and charge a sliding scale to help the patient afford a realistic fee. (For a list of psychotherapy centres see the Appendix.)

Psychoanalysis

Psychoanalysis is the technique of investigation and therapy devised by Freud for the treatment of neurotic and other disorders. Unlike the psychotherapy just described it entails seeing the patient for five times a week or more over a period of years. The term 'psychoanalysis' is widely used but often in an inexact sense. Strictly speaking it should only be used to describe an orthodox Freudian analysis. This process is practised by a psychoanalyst, that is a medical or lay person who has fulfilled the training requirements of the British Psycho Analytical Association and has himself undergone a minimum period of personal psychoanalysis as part of his or her training.

Although both individual and group psychotherapy may use Freudian theory, they should not be confused with psychoanalysis *per se*. Jung and Adler, both pupils of Freud, broke away and founded their own methods of therapy. These are called analytical psychotherapy and individual psychology, respectively.

Patients undertaking psychoanalysis present a wide variety of personality difficulties, ranging from neurotic phobias to delinquent behaviour. Many have had other forms of psychiatric treatment. Before clinical criteria are considered patients must be able to afford the time and money, for it is not available on the NHS. The Institute of Psycho Analysis in London accepts some patients on a reduced fee. Most analyses are conducted on a private basis and, like private psychotherapy, fees are usually on a sliding scale depending on the patient's income.

GROUP PSYCHOTHERAPY

Unlike individual psychotherapy the main focus of interest in group psychotherapy is the inter-relationships within the group. Individual problems are shared and members can often see their personal difficulties reflected in the relationships within the group. Each member is then able to contribute his comments and the therapist's role is to interpret the problems that invariably arise within the group.

In many ways this kind of therapy has great advantages over individual psychotherapy for those with marked social and interpersonal relationship difficulties. Indeed, some workers would argue that this ought to be the treatment of choice for those patients whose main problems centre around communication and social relationships. Many of the basic concepts of psychoanalytical theory and a whole body of theoretical knowledge of group work has evolved in the understanding of group processes. It is the group therapist's role to interpret resistive and defensive behaviour and so facilitate interaction. Group therapy sessions are usually held once or twice weekly on an out-patient basis and last for about one and a half hours. Group therapy can continue over a period of years depending on the needs and progress of individual patients. Most psychiatric settings practise group work and often these are modified versions of group psychotherapy to help patients develop the capacity to gain confidence and discuss problems with others.

MARITAL AND FAMILY THERAPY

A great deal has been written about marital and family therapy and there is a lot of interest in it by social workers and psychotherapists on both sides of the Atlantic. It is an area of constant development and growth. In this section we do not aspire to a new construction, rather an overview of the more common approaches that exist at present.

It was Jung who first alluded to family centred therapeutic intervention, in relation to childhood disturbances. He stated quite clearly that where there are childhood disturbances these pointed to underlying conflicts in the marital relationship of the parents and unless these were resolved, the child could not gain a full resolution of his difficulties.

Marriage and mental health

A wide range of evidence, particularly from the USA, has highlighted the relationship between mental health and marriage. Married people tend to have lower rates of hospitalisation, lower rates of out-patient treatment, lower rates of alcoholism and of suicide. Married people tend to live longer than the unmarried.

In recent years, sociologists have mounted a critique of the family, noting its historical associations with property rights, the State, and male/female hierarchical roles. The 'nuclear' family has been questioned in terms of its role as the nurturer of children. Certainly other cultures have quite different networks and roles. The value of these alternative patterns for mental health in our culture has not yet been firmly established. Recent statistics in *Marriage 1983* (1984) for the UK indicate that the incidence of marriage is as high as ever, including rates of remarriage amongst the divorced. A note needs to be added that divorce tends to be highest amongst the unemployed, particularly the unskilled, and the young (under 29s).

Research in both the USA and the UK (see below) has emphasised the ways in which children of parents with marital conflicts are affected detrimentally—both as children, but also as adults in later life (USA: Kellam (1977); Kelly and Wallerstein (1975); McDermott (1968); Tolley (1976); Bentler and Newcomb (1978); Gregory (1965); Alkon (1971); UK: Bowlby (1969); Rutter (1971); Hong Kong: Lo (1969)).

Such marital conflicts could be externally visible to the child, such as divorce and separation, or internally felt, such as discord and disharmony. There does, therefore, seem to be a clear indication that in most cases of childhood disturbance, intervention in the form of family therapy should be considered. Where there are no children, but the marriage partners are wanting to work together and resolve their conflicts, then marital therapy is indicated.

Theoretical approaches to family therapy

As with any form of therapeutic intervention, there are as many approaches to family therapy as there are family therapists. Nevertheless, there are some essential theoretical concepts that inform and go to create the various 'schools' of family therapy. We set these out below. For a more detailed exposition of each proponent, we recommend that interested readers refer to the works of the clinicians and writers who are named in the bibliography at the end of this chapter.

Psychoanalytic approaches
Practitioners of this approach tend to use group psychotherapeutic methods, within a framework of human development and group interaction seen from the psychoanalytic perspective. The group

analysts Foulkes and Bion generated much original work in the area of group psychotherapy. In the field of family therapy, the group analysts' methods have been drawn on, but also contributed to in great measure, particularly in the UK by the Tavistock School, with such clinicians as Bowlby, Bentovim, Byng-Hall, Dare and Skynner.

Structural approaches

Structuralists view the family as a living structure, where systems and sub-systems exist, and are negotiated between family members. Therapeutic intervention aims at helping the family redefine these structures, reallocating power, and encouraging flexible roles and boundaries. Chief exponent of this model is Minuchin.

Communication approaches

This approach views difficulties within the family equilibrium as arising from difficulties in communication. Communications are either faulty, unclear, or made in the form of a 'double bind'. The therapist's task is to help communications pass in a more clear and direct way. In the USA proponents of this approach have been the Palo Alto Group (Bateson *et al.*), and Satir. In the UK Laing, Esterson and Cooper have focussed on this approach.

Behavioural approaches

Behaviour modification techniques have been used by some family therapists as an approach to therapy. This focusses on the symptoms of a difficulty, and attempts both to alter the symptoms and encourage more acceptance of the difficulty. One simple example of this would be in a situation of marital therapy, where the husband agrees to empty the dustbins, while the wife in response agrees to make the tea more often.

We have given above some of the main strands of theory as it applies to family therapy. We would emphasise however, that these need not be rigid approaches, and indeed in more and more instances, a combination of approaches—or an 'integrative' model—is used. In addition the personality of the therapist(s) will play a great part in the therapeutic process—whether he is active, or passive; controlling, or enabling; noisy, or silent; perhaps more than dogmatic technique, it is important for the therapist to be aware of his own personality, and the effect that this will have on the family. Conversely, the effect the family is having on himself and his choice of approach will give him clear information about the feelings and pressures which exist within that family. This is discussed in more detail in Chapter 12.

General considerations

Any form of family therapy will need to address the following issues:

1. Venue. This is usually the clinician's office or consulting room.
2. Whom to invite. Some family therapists feel that as many family members that exist should come—others that only those who dwell under the same roof should be present. Certainly the more that come, the clearer the dynamic that will emerge.
3. Stated purpose. The therapist will need to demonstrate a belief that the meeting has something valuable to offer. He will need to make the purpose of the meeting quite clear. Will the family be expected to sit and talk freely? Might they be expected to take part in 'action' sessions such as sculpting or psychodrama? ('Family sculpting' is a technique where a family member will put others into the positions, physically and in terms of proximity, that he feels best describes the situation in the household. 'Psychodrama' is the acting out of some important life event, in order to give participants more understanding of the event, its causes and effects.)
4. Frequency. Weekly? Fortnightly? Monthly? This needs to be clarified with the family. Many experienced therapists feel that some space needs to be left between meetings to give the family time to digest the content of the sessions. Skynner (1976) suggests a three week gap between sessions.
5. Duration. Weeks? Months? Years? This cannot be determined at the outset. An initial contract—say of six meetings—may be helpful, reviewable at the last session, or before, if needs be.
6. To conduct the therapy alone or with a co-worker? Increasingly, family therapy sessions are led by two therapists so that a wider range of interventions is made possible. In many child guidance clinics, one-way screens and videos are now common practice, with observers taking an advisory role as the sessions take place.

Indications and contra-indications

For family therapy to work, there must be a willingness for the family to come together, and work towards resolving their conflicts. They must have a wish to put into words their feelings and views. If there are severe degrees of disturbance—say family violence—then the initial assessment must question whether this might be exacerbated in the short term, rendering a vulnerable family member at risk. In some instances, recent developments in local authority resources have enabled complete families to be taken into care in a residential setting. This can have value for very disturbed or deprived families.

Where there is a high incidence of financial poverty, family therapy may not have a good prognostic outcome. The family may be under too many pressures from other sources to believe that they will benefit from family therapy.

Family therapy with adult families

Where there is a disturbance within a particular child, the initial assessment will always need to take account of the family and community dimension. In many cases of mental illness, however, an adult mentally ill person will be living at home with his parents. Recent research has shown that specific types of family therapy can be very useful in these situations, both in terms of reducing relapse rates, and also in terms of symptom alleviation.

In particular, the work of Leff and Vaughan in the field of schizophrenia has indicated that in many instances, where a person with schizophrenia is living at home with relatives, there exists what Leff and Vaughan define as 'high expressed emotion' (HEE) interaction. We have discussed this in Chapter 1, in the section on schizophrenia. By careful therapeutic intervention aimed at reducing HEE comments, the person with the schizophrenic illness (the 'identified patient' in Satir's helpful definition) can be supported and their suffering alleviated; whilst the other family members can be helped to accept and understand their mutual difficulties.

Other considerations

It needs to be borne in mind that where the identified patient receives all the attention within the family, and the patient is a child with brothers and sisters, the siblings themselves may feel neglected, begin to 'act out', and thus develop behaviour problems themselves, creating a 'problem family'. Where there is a handicapped child within the family this can often happen and efforts will need to be made to help the parents come to terms with the handicap whilst not excluding the needs of other family members.

Case illustration

The father of three boys suffered from a schizophrenic illness. His wife struggled to ensure that their children did not know about this illness, concealing from their children her husband's contact with his social worker, and even trying to conceal the fact of his eventual hospital admission. She used all sorts of seemingly valid justifications for this concealment: 'the boys are too young'; 'my husband will get over it'; 'I cannot bear the shame'; 'the children were told their daddy had had to go away on business'.

Soon however, the children sensed that a great deception was taking place, but could not make sense of it, nor of their feelings. Gradually they began to put on considerable weight over the ensuing months, as a way of compensating for the lack of emotional attention from their parents. This increase in weight was used as the initial focus of family therapy intervention. The social worker was able to persuade the husband and wife to take part in these sessions with their children, and slowly they began to feel more confident in speaking frankly about the hidden illness which their father had been suffering. The children's weight increase halted, and truancy, which had been insidiously developing alongside their eating difficulty, ceased.

Some criticisms?

Critics of family therapy point out that it can tend to be adult oriented. Children are often outnumbered by adults present. They may not be as verbally articulate. Children may feel frightened of punishment outside of the session if they say the 'wrong thing'. Family therapy approaches may not be able to make contact with some of the deeper, unconscious conflicts that are often the source of difficult behaviour. Parents themselves may be reluctant to talk about intimate sexual matters in front of their children.

BEHAVIOUR THERAPY

Behaviour therapy has developed from the early work on conditioning undertaken by Pavlov, together with insights and methods gleaned from modern psychological learning theories. Unlike psychoanalytical theory, behaviour therapy is based on the assumption that neurotic symptoms are a result of faulty learning. Behaviour therapy is therefore aimed at helping the patient to unlearn these morbid fears and learn new behaviour which is personally and socially more acceptable. It is not concerned with the underlying cause of the symptoms but focusses on observable symptoms and behaviour patterns.

Behaviour therapists concentrate much more on the patient's present situation than on his past, although important events are noted and are often used when developing a treatment programme. The patient–

therapist relationship is important in that it is useful as 'a positive reinforcer'—if the patient likes the therapist he is more inclined to change his behaviour to gain the approval of the therapist. Behaviour therapists tend to be more directive than other therapists, while at the same time trying to encourage the patient to play a more active role, both in designing the treatment programme and carrying out practical assignments.

Several techniques have been developed to treat a wide range of psychiatric disorders and these are summarised below. As this approach derives from clinical psychological research, most of those involved in the therapy and supervision are clinical psychologists. However, other people who are involved in the daily life of the patient may also play a major role in the treatment; these can include nurse, parent, teacher and social worker.

Desensitisation (reciprocal inhibition)

This model was first employed by Joseph Wolpe (1958) with patients suffering from anxiety-related problems. He found that if patients were gradually exposed to objects or situations which they feared, while at the same time engaged in pleasant activity (in Wolpe's case, he taught them deep muscle relaxation) this tended to inhibit anxiety.

Wolpe encouraged his patients first to imagine the objects and situations which aroused fear. The patient was given a graded series of anxiety making situations, from the least to the most disturbing. Over the progress of the sessions, the patient begins gradually to tolerate the most disturbing situations as he climbs the hierarchy, first in imagination then in real life situations.

The patient's ability to experience these stressful events in imagination was often followed by diminished anxiety when faced with them in real life situations. This therapy is most successful if there is a specific, clearly defined fear or impulse, for example, a phobia of insects or of flying. It is not so effective in the more generalised fears like agoraphobia.

Implosive therapy (flooding)

Systematic desensitisation exposes the patient to his fears in a gradual way. Implosive therapy on the other hand, involves exposure to the phobic situation in a more immediate way. The patient is encouraged to imagine himself in the most anxiety provoking situation. This is based on the view that extinction of the anxiety condition will take place if the patient can be prevented from avoiding or escaping from the anxiety making situation. The therapist continues to provide additional images and cues to help maximise the patient's anxiety. Usually, the treatment session ends when the patient imagines the worst situation and all the therapist's efforts to increase the patient's anxiety cease, and the patient's anxiety level falls.

In the flooding techniques, the patient is taken by the therapist to the phobic situation in real life, but does not get involved in the stimulus augmentation. In each case it is important that the session continues until the anxiety level falls, otherwise no extinction will take place.

Assertion training

Many of our clients suffer from a crippling inability to express themselves in social situations. Some find it difficult to ask for something which is their due. Many experience untold misery and find social contact embarrassing and difficult, and eventually withdraw and lead isolated lives. These are some of the clients who might benefit from this kind of behaviour therapy.

Clients are encouraged to express their feelings to others in a gradual way, thereby making each new situation less and less frightening. The result of such an approach has a good deal in common with that which we have described in the desensitisation approach. Inhibited individuals are helped to take a bolder attitude to social situations, taking risks and gradually learning to enjoy self-expression without always fearing the rejection of others.

Operant conditioning

This type of treatment was first introduced in the USA by Steiner in 1953. Attempts are made to shape behaviour by rewards and punishments, and these are based largely on work with severely disturbed patients in mental hospitals.

Perhaps the best known and most extensive approach is the token economy system. Studies by Ayllon and Azrin in 1968 demonstrated how the behaviour of extremely regressed patients could be changed or modified by this approach. Patients were given rewards for desired behaviour; for example, for good self-care where they have made their own beds and kept themselves clean. These rewards were given in the form of plastic tokens which could later be exchanged for special privileges or extra visits to the canteen to buy chocolate, etc. The rewarding of desired behaviour and the ignoring or penalising of undesired behaviour, increased the frequency of the former and diminished that of the latter. It was shown that this simple principle reduced antisocial behaviour on the ward. It also increased staff morale because of the creative involvement of the staff.

This behavioural approach is now used in the everyday management of rehabilitation wards of many mental hospitals in this country. The modifying of the most difficult antisocial aspects of patients' behaviour enables them to become more acceptable to others, and eases their adjustment into the community on discharge.

REFERENCES AND FURTHER READING

Physical treatment

American Psychiatric Association (1978). *Electroconvulsive Therapy*. Task Force Report 14.

Bridges P. K., Goktepe E. O., Maratos J. (1973). A Comparative review of patients with obsessional neurosis and with depression treated by psychosurgery. *Br. J. Psychiatry*; **123**: 663–5.

Bridges P. K. (1984). Psychosurgery and the Mental Health Act Commission. *Bull. R. Coll. Psychiatrists*; **August**: 146–7.

Claridge G. S. (1972). *Drugs and Human Behaviour*. London: Penguin.

Crow T. J. (1979). The scientific status of electro-convulsive therapy (editorial). *Psychological Med.*; **9**: 401–8.

Field L. H., Williams M. (1970). The hormonal treatment of sexual offenders. *Med. Science and the Law*; **10(1)**: 27–30.

Fisher R. B., Christie G. A. (1982). *A Dictionary of Drugs*. London: Paladin.

Laitinen L., Livingston K. (1973). *Surgical Approaches in Psychiatry*. Lancaster: Medical & Technical Publishing Co. Ltd.

Loucas K., Bancroft J., Tennent G., Cass J. (1974). The control of deviant sexual behaviour by drugs. *Br. J. Psychiatry*; **125**: 310–15.

Sargent W., Slater E. (1972). *An Introduction to Physical Methods of Treatment in Psychiatry*. Edinburgh: Churchill-Livingstone.

Schurr P. H. (1969). Leucotomy. *Br. J. Hosp. Med.*, **October**: 1712–15.

Psychological treatment

Alkon D. I. (1971). Parental deprivation. *Acta Psychiatrica Scandinavia Suppl.*; **233**: 7–8.

Ayllon T., Azrin N. H. (1968). *The Token Economy*. Hemel Hempstead: Appleton–Century–Crofts.

Barrett M., McIntosh M. (1982). *The Anti-Social Family*. London: Verso Editions.

Bateson G. (1978). *Steps to an Ecology of Mind*. London: Granada.

Bentler P. M., Newcomb M. D. (1978). Longitudinal study of marital success and failure. *J. Consulting and Clinical Psychology*; **46**: 1053–70.

Berke J. H. (1977). *The Butterfly Man*. London: Hutchinson.

Bettleheim B. (1977). *The Children of the Dream*. London: Paladin.

Bowlby J. (1969). *Attachment*. London: Hogarth Press.

Ellenberger H. F. (1970). *The Discovery of the Unconscious*. London: Allen Lane Penguin.

Eysenck H. J. (1976). *Case Studies in Behaviour Therapy*. London: Routledge & Kegan Paul.

Fransella F. (1971). *Inquiring Man*. London: Penguin.

Gregory I. (1965). Anterospective data following childhood loss of parent. *Arch. General Psychiatry*; **13**: 110–12.

Guntrip H. (1973). *Psychoanalytic Theory, Therapy and the Self*. New York: Basic Books.

Herson R., ed. (1975). *Progress in Behaviour Modification*. New York: Academic Press.

Holland S. (1984). Loss, rage and oppression. *Pam Smith Memorial Lecture* (unpubl.).

Jung C. G. (1954). The development of personality. In *Collected Works, Volume 17*. London: Routledge & Kegan Paul.

Kellam S. G., Ensminger M. E., Turner R. J. (1977). Family structure and the mental health of children. *Arch. General Psychiatry*; **34**: 1012–22.

Kelly J. B., Wallerstein J. S. (1975). The effects of parental divorce: the experience of the child in late latency. *Am. J. Orthopsychiatry*; **45**: 253–8.

Lo W. H. (1969). Aetiological factors in childhood neurosis. *Br. J. Psychiatry*; **115**: 889–94.

McDermott J. F. (1968). Parental divorce in early childhood. *Am. J. Psychiatry*; **124**: 118–26.

Meichenbaum D. (1977). *Cognitive Behaviour Modification*. Morriston: General Learning Press.

Meyer V., Chesser E. S. (1970). *Behaviour Therapy in Clinical Psychiatry*. London: Penguin.

Minuchin S. (1977). *Families and Family Therapy*. London: Tavistock Publications.

Mitchell J. (1978). *Psychoanalysis and Feminism*. London: Penguin.

Mitchell J. (1984). *Women: the Longest Revolution*. London: Virago.

Office of Population Censuses and Surveys (1984). *Monitor: Marriages 1983*. London: HMSO.

Roszak B., Roszak T., eds. (1969). *Masculine/Feminine*. New York: Harper & Row.

Rush A. J., *et al.* (1977). Comparative efficacy of cognitive therapy and pharmacotherapy in the treatment of depressed outpatients. *Cognitive Therapy and Research*; **1**: 17–37.

Rutter M. (1971). Parent–child separation: psychological effects on children. *J. Child Psychology and Psychiatry*; **12**: 233–60.

Salzberger-Wittenberg I. (1970). *Psycho-Analytic Insight and Relationships*. London: Routledge & Kegan Paul.

Satir V. (1978). *Conjoint Family Therapy*. London: Condor Books.

Skinner B. F. (1972). *Beyond Freedom and Dignity*. London: Penguin.

Skynner A. C. R. (1976). *One Flesh: Separate Persons*. London: Constable.

Social Trends 15 (1985). *The Times*, 10 Jan.

Storr A. (1979). *The Art of Psychotherapy*. London: Secker & Warburg and William Heinemann Medical Books.

Taylor–Segraves R. (1982). *Marital Therapy*. London: Plenum Medical.

Tennant J. W., ed. (1980). *Current Trends in Treatment in Psychiatry*. London: Pitman.

Thompson S., Kahn J. (1970). *The Group Process as a Helping Technique*. Oxford: Pergamon.

Tolley K. (1976). Anti-social behaviour and social alienation post-divorce. *Am. J. Orthopsychiatry*; **46**: 33–43.

Walczak Y., Burns S. (1984). *Divorce: The Child's Point of View*. London: Harper & Row.

Walrond–Skinner S., ed. (1981). *Developments in Family Therapy*. London: Tavistock Publications.

Walton H. (1971). *Small Group Psychotherapy*. London: Penguin.

Wilson E. (1977). *Women and the Welfare State*. London: Tavistock Publications.

Wolberg L. R., Aronson M. L., eds. (1980). *Group and Family Therapy*. New York: Brunner/Mazel.

Wolpe J. (1958). *Psychotherapy by Reciprocal Inhibition*. Stanford: Stanford University Press.

Wolpe J. (1969). *The Practice of Behaviour Therapy*. Oxford: Pergamon.

Chapter 10

The Multi-disciplinary Team

Within the hospital setting the multi-disciplinary team consists of a range of professionals, including the doctor, nurse, occupational therapist, psychologist, social worker, art therapist, industrial therapist, remedial gymnast, psychotherapist, religious minister, community psychiatric nurse, and other medical specialists, such as physiotherapists, dentists, etc.

The members of the multi-disciplinary team keep in close liaison, the core members meeting together at weekly ward rounds to monitor the patients' care and progress. Ward rounds are usually attended regularly by the consultant psychiatrist, junior doctor, nurses, occupational therapist, social worker and psychologist.

Ultimate responsibility for a patient's care and medical treatment while in hospital lies with the consultant psychiatrist who, in terms of the Mental Health Act 1983, is designated the 'Responsible Medical Officer'. The consultant psychiatrist may also be a specialist—in child psychiatry, psychotherapy (consultant psychotherapist), elderly mentally infirm (consultant psychogeriatrician), or criminological psychiatry (forensic psychiatrist).

The tasks of each member of the multi-disciplinary team complement one another so as to provide care, support and treatment to the whole person. The structure and functions of the team can be seen in Fig. 10.1. It will be observed that the social worker (and religious minister) is responsible to two masters: one within the hospital (the consultant), and another outside (their own department). This enables the social worker to act as a 'bridge' and a link between patient and community; however, few people can serve two masters without experiencing stress and conflict in the process. Inevitably these arise and there are no easy answers to the dilemma.

In the community, the multi-disciplinary team is more diverse, and diffused throughout several agencies and individuals. Here the social worker is often called upon to play an important role as coordinator of resources, in this way taking over the role of the institution. This role is

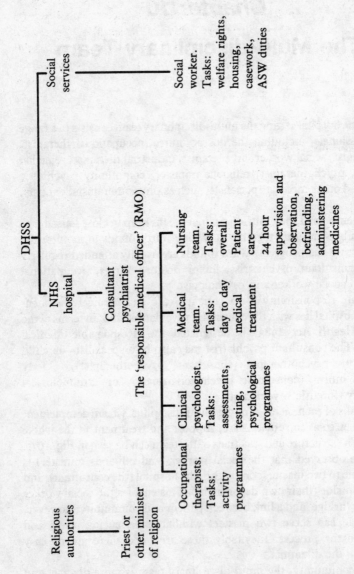

Fig. 10.1 The multi-disciplinary team in the clinical setting.

emphasised in the philosophy of community care underlying the 1983 Act, and also in the closure of large mental hospitals which is now taking place. It remains to be seen whether social services will be able to raise sufficient financial and personal resources to meet the challenge of community care. The coordinating function of the social worker can be illustrated diagrammatically as shown in Fig. 10.2. It may be that as the philosophy of community care is developed, there is a concomitant increase in the involvement of social work clients in the planning of resource allocation and service delivery.

INTERDISCIPLINARY ISSUES

When working within the multi-disciplinary team, or even when working jointly on an *ad hoc* basis (say in joint social work–GP assessments) conflicts can arise. These are often impossible to deal with at that moment, since they are often at the point of crisis. Thus it can be of some help to prepare ourselves for them in advance. The main issues which tend to arise as sources of conflict are ones of authority and information.

Authority

As we have already questioned above: who is in control? In a joint social work–GP visit, is the person being assessed primarily our client, or the

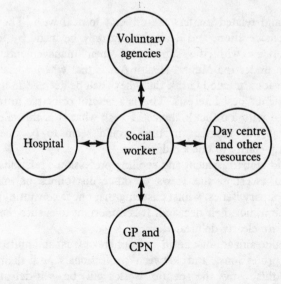

Fig. 10.2 The coordinating function of the social worker.

GP's patient? Clearly he is both. But if the GP wishes him to be admitted to hospital against his will and we do not agree with this recommendation, this can put us under considerable pressure to comply with the GP's recommendation. In the hospital setting, where social workers work on wards, to whom do they owe allegiance? Their own social work department, or the consultant who is, after all within the hospital, the 'responsible medical officer'?

Information

The second major area of difficulty can be in the area of information. It manifests itself in such matters as open records, information sharing between disciplines, telephone confidentiality and letter-writing. Our client may be living in a hostel, not taking medication, and breaking down towards a psychotic episode. Is it within our professional code to contact his GP if he does not consent to our so doing? If we do not the likelihood is that our client will become floridly mentally ill. If we do, we will be breaking confidentiality.

A second type of difficulty can arise when we have on our case notes confidential letters or reports written to us by other professionals, say, a psychiatric report. If our client wishes to see his file, do we allow him to do so but remove the confidential documents written by other disciplines? Is this merely paying lip service to the principle of open records?

These and related matters are difficult to deal with. They require careful consideration, and decisions can only be made by individual social workers with the support of their management. A clear protection under the Mental Health Act is that where social workers make decisions 'in good faith', then they shall be deemed to have acted in their clients' best interests. This is a helpful principle to remember when faced with a difficult choice. To ask what is in this client's best interests at this moment in time would seem to be one way of introducing clarity to one's judgement.

To avoid embarrassment and spoiling professional relationships it is helpful to ascertain the views of other disciplines on matters of interdisciplinary issues, whilst ensuring that one is consulting them for their opinion, not their decision. It is important to ensure that lines of authority are clearly delineated.

The goal to aim at must be an atmosphere of trust and mutual respect between professions, and between professionals and their clients. Without this, any therapeutic work will be self-defeating and confusing.

VOLUNTEERS

Volunteers are being called upon to play an increasing variety of roles within the mental health field. Advantages in using volunteers are that they can bring a fresh approach to our sometimes rigid structures. Some clients find it easier to relate to non-authoritarian figures. Volunteers often have more time and are under less pressure than the paid and responsible social worker. However, the use of volunteers calls for an increased input from the employing agency in terms of training, ongoing support, and monitoring. This needs to be taken into account when considering the use of volunteers.

Settings

There tend to be three types of settings where volunteers can be found:

1. Where the purpose of the agency is to satisfy the needs of its own members. For example, a self-help group.
2. Where the agency is satisfying a need which is not being recognised by statutory services—the 'voluntary sector'. For example, a neighbourhood advice centre. These types of organisations will probably use a mixture of paid and non-paid workers.
3. Where the agency uses volunteers to supplement its professional role for particular tasks. For example, hospitals.

Points to consider

Clearly, when considering taking on volunteers, any local union agreements will need to be examined and honoured. In addition, volunteers are in the main, untrained people. They may be young people wanting social work experience prior to training; they may be unemployed; they may be retired. They are not a homogeneous group. Therefore, tasks will need to be clearly explained, feedback obtained, and time set aside for both supervision and training. These might profitably take the form of discussion groups.

The employing agency will need to ensure that its own aims, methods and boundaries are explained to the volunteer, preferably in writing (say, a handout or duplicated sheet). This will help the volunteer avoid transgressing boundaries inadvertently. For example, in a social work agency it will generally be the policy for social workers and volunteers not to take clients to their own homes. Volunteers will need to know this, if they are not to become personally involved with their clients.

Selection

Volunteers will need to be selected carefully. Usually, references will be obtained. Most volunteers will be sincerely wanting to help other people. Very occasionally, people have become volunteers for other motives, and have abused their positions, with damaging results for clients and agencies.

REFERENCES AND FURTHER READING

Alinsky S. D. (1972). *Rules for Radicals*. New York: Vintage Books.

Batten T. R. (1975). *The Non-Directive Approach in Group and Community Work*. Oxford: Oxford University Press.

Cassee E. (1975). Therapeutic behaviour, hospital culture and communication. In *A Sociology of Medical Practice* (Cox C., Mead A., eds.). West Drayton: Collier Macmillan.

Department of Health and Social Security (1978). *Social Services Teams: The Practitioner's View* (Stevenson O., Parsloe P., eds.). London: HMSO.

Directory of Projects: England and Wales 1982–3 (1982). London: Taylor Hall Publishing, in association with MIND, NACRO and FARE.

Etzioni A. (1971). *A Comparative Analysis of Complex Organisations*. West Drayton: Free Press.

Evans E. H. (1981). Multidisciplinary teams in geriatric wards: myth or reality. *J. Advanced Nursing*; 6: 205–14.

Fisher M., Newton C., Sainsbury E. (1984). *Mental Health Social Work Observed*. London: NISW Library No. 45.

Halmos P. (1978). *The Personal and the Political*. London: Hutchinson.

Handy C. B. (1980). *Understanding Organisations*. London: Penguin.

Illich I., Zoca I. K., McKnight J., Caplan J., Shaiken H. (1977). *Disabling Professions*. London: Marion Boyars.

Kadushin A. (1977). *Consultation in Social Work*. Columbia: Columbia University Press.

Miles A. (1977). Staff relations in psychiatric hospitals. *Br. J. Psychiatry*; 130: 84–8.

NCVO (1982). *Voluntary Organisations: An NCVO Directory (1982–3)*. London: Bedford Square Press.

Whyte W. F. (1969). *Organisational Behaviour*. Toronto: Irwin Publishing.

World Health Organisation (1973). *Psychiatry and Primary Health Care*. Copenhagen: WHO.

Chapter 11

The Long-term Care of the Mentally Ill

Social workers encounter a lot of mentally ill people in situations of crisis. We rarely have the time to continue or renew our contact beyond the crisis point. Other statutory duties must be fulfilled, other crises take priority; yet few episodes of mental illness are isolated incidents. The experience of mental illness leaves a profound impact on the sufferer, in terms of self-image, stigma and disorientation. More than this, however, once a person has suffered a mental illness, it is very likely that they will suffer it again at some point in their lives; relapse, or chronicity, more often than not follow an episode of mental illness.

We are aware here of the danger of labelling; together with the issues that arise from the political–philosophical debate about the place of mental illness in society. What we see, however, are the destructive effects of mental illness when it persists in the lives of our clients. This is where we are focussing our attention in the present work.

Medical treatment and social intervention can play important roles in ameliorating much of the distress and the more destructive effects of a long-term, or relapsing, mental illness. Some of the ways in which this can be achieved by social workers are given below.

WORK

Long-term mental illness may well mean that the sufferer can take on only light, non-stressful work, if at all. In the current social and economic conditions, it is probably more true to say that few employers will 'risk' having a mentally ill person on their payroll.

UNEMPLOYMENT

Unemployment affects everyone. Not only those who are on the vast dole queue but those who, for one reason or another, are unable to work. For example, the mentally ill.

For most of us the routine and structure of the work situation gives us a feeling of identity. It tests our capacity to exercise judgement and to carry responsibility. The work we do enables us to be creative and our internal and external reality is continually reaffirmed. In short, our work not only satisfies a material need, it also gives us a fundamental sense of self-worth.

In a study carried out by Jahoda in Austria in the thirties, unemployment was seen as a social evil. He found that men who were unemployed over long periods lost some of their sense of reality; they also lost their sense of time, for example clocks in their home were not wound up. They became unpunctual for meals and a general sense of irrationality appeared. For example, some bought unnecessary things instead of food. Although they had time on their hands, they did not read or were unable to use this time for leisure; libraries became almost deserted.

In a more recent study Antebi (Meacher, 1979) found that 81% of those unemployed for more than six weeks complained of sleeplessness, depression and physical symptoms during the period out of work.

EMPLOYMENT

Where clients are in work, social workers can, with their clients' permission, liaise with employers to ensure that jobs are held open for the patient who relapses. This will need to be done discreetly, since certain unsympathetic employers may be afraid to continue links with an employee known to be 'mentally ill'. Social workers in areas of high unemployment may be able to play a coordinating or even educative role in this respect: links with local community work groups and trades councils may be one approach to these matters.

Alternatively it may be important for a client to leave, or transfer out of, a post which is too stressful, as stress can precipitate relapse of a mental illness. In the present economic climate, with the decline of industry, people are coming to face redundancy or early retirement at an increasingly younger age. Loss of a life-long job can be a major precipitant in the onset of a depressive illness.

DAY CARE

If a client does not have a job, day care in the form of a day centre can offer support and rehabilitation. Nevertheless, certain groups of patients, especially those suffering from schizophrenia, may find even low-key day centres too threatening and not be able to accept the demands of being a member of a group. For example, in the middle of an interview for a day centre place, one ex-hospital patient got up and left 'to buy some fags'. He never returned to the interview and by not doing so made his position plain.

These types of feelings and reactions need to be respected and the client not forced into situations of which he is unsure. The schizophrenia sufferer especially, needs an atmosphere of acceptance where few, or no, demands are made.

HOUSING

When a client becomes mentally ill or relapses his normal responsibilities are neglected. The social worker can play a role in remembering them for the client. Thus, the mentally ill person easily and often loses his accommodation through non-payment of rent, or 'bad' behaviour (foul language, abusiveness, violence). The provision of a secure base is important for us all, no less in the case of the mentally ill person.

The types of non-hospital accommodation currently available for the mentally ill, depending upon the resources of the area in which they live, are: hostels, group homes, therapeutic communities, adult foster care (or 'boarding out'), elderly people's homes (commonly referred to as Part 3 accommodation, after Part 3 of the National Assistance Act 1948) or a flat of their own. The type of accommodation that is sought will depend upon the availability of accommodation, how much and what type, of support the person needs.

Adult foster care can be a particularly successful type of placement. It can offer a person a room of his own, but with a supportive structure in the form of a family, who are themselves receiving back-up from their own support social worker (i.e. the family's support social worker will be their own advocate, but the person whom they are fostering will also retain a social worker of his own). This system requires commitment from the local authority social services in finding families, and providing long-term support for them, as well as for the person placed with them. In addition, families need careful selection in order to ensure that there will be no abuse of a potentially lucrative area of private enterprise.

Experiments are now being made with 'core and cluster' settings, where several individual flats or bedsits housing mentally ill people are grouped in close proximity both to each other, and also to a local day care resource. This provides the opportunity for private, non-intrusive, non-institutional homes, with ease of access to both an organised resource, and also other people with similar backgrounds. This can encourage self-help and the formation of informal, non-professional relationships.

FINANCE

Being unable to work, often spending long periods 'on the sick', and losing track of their budgeting system, means that the mentally ill are nearly always short of money; and in many instances will not even have had their DHSS entitlement. At other times, they have had their state entitlements, but because of their confusion, have forgotten that they have had it. The hypomanic patient may well have spent all of his money and more, in a manic spree. Many patients do not even claim their statutory entitlements because of the depressed nature of their illness. Social workers can play a role here in helping their clients regain some control of their financial affairs. This calls for skills of advocacy, and also patience. It can be very infuriating to spend a day on the telephone to the DHSS chasing a client's 'missing' giro, only to find that he had received it three weeks previously and had given it away to a stranger in the street! A client's attitude to his financial state can often be a reflection of his internal state.

FAMILIES

Social workers can have an important role to play in supporting the family of the long-term mentally ill. Where the client is a child of the family, the parents often feel guilty and responsible, as if their offspring is a failure and sometimes, a taboo. Pressure can be put on to the client from other family members to get better 'somehow', get out of bed, get a job, pull himself together. Unfortunately these moral imperatives tend to be counter-productive. Social work intervention can focus on helping the parents to come to terms with their feelings of guilt. Once this has been addressed (not dealt with, because it will still remain as an undercurrent and a recurring theme) the family members can be helped to limit critical comments and keep them to a minimum. Research has shown that critical comments from any source—family, friends, social workers, adult carers—drastically precipitate relapses for schizophrenia sufferers.

Where the mentally ill client is a parent, husband or wife, social work needs to be focussed on helping:

1. The client to come to terms with the threatened capacity (i.e. the capacity to be the breadwinner, or to be the loving parent).
2. The partner to come to terms with the loss of their loved one (who may never be the same again).
3. The children to come to terms with the loss of the parent as they knew him.

In recent years there has been the development of self-help groups to help families cope with the disruptive problems that a sick member can create. The social worker may be able to refer families to the local groups, as such difficulties are likely to be long term and require maximum support.

THE CASEWORK RELATIONSHIP

Perhaps the key to the long-term community care of the mentally ill is for the social worker to be able to establish a consistent, if low-key, relationship with the mentally ill person on their caseload. Mental illness consists of confusion, sadness, distress, panic and mis-communication. The mentally ill person can be unrewarding— ungrateful, angry, rude or incoherent. It is sometimes hard for us to remember that these are, in fact, signs of psychic pain. We can, if we are not sensitive to these issues, simply take offence or feel hurt, or feel failures ourselves, and thus back off from our clients. These, too, are real and important reactions and will be discussed in the next chapter. Our emphasis here, however, is that the client is also wrestling with these feelings about himself. If we can withstand his distress and destructive feelings, then we may be able to transmit to the patient some sense of self-worth and internal strength that may help him in his own struggle against his illness. This can be invaluable to a client's mental health, even if it takes a toll on ours. Yet it need not take a toll on ours. It does not help the client to become immersed or lost in his illness with him. In fact, it may make him feel more confused. The skill of the therapeutic relationship seems to be one of maintaining some sense of being available to the client, while gradually working towards leaving the onus with him to contact us when he needs us. We may only need to see him once a month, or once a year. This may be for one hour or for five minutes; as long as the client knows that we are there, and cannot be overwhelmed by the forces that overwhelm him, he will be enabled to feel contained and understood. There is nothing more important than this.

INSTITUTIONALISATION: THE 'OLD LONG STAY' MENTALLY ILL

Hand in hand with the Mental Health Act 1983 has come the present policy of closure for the large mental hospitals throughout England. This reinforces the concept of community care, and will place an increased burden on social services in the years to come.

Apart from the long-term mentally ill in the community, social workers are increasingly called upon to work with the patient who has been, or will be, discharged from hospital after being there as an in-patient for many years, decades in some cases. These patients, who can be classified as the 'old long stay' mentally ill, are institutionalised.

Early research on the so-called 'institutional neurosis' (institutionalisation) amongst orphaned children in formal care settings (such as children's homes, refugee camps) demonstrated that such settings induced in their residents an attitude of dependency upon the institution. The institutionalised person feels a closer bond to the physical bricks, mortar and regime of the institution than to its staff.

There are obvious reasons for this dependency. The institution provides total, 24 hour care. It never closes. It never goes away. It is more consistent than other human resources. It can absorb a wide range of behaviour, and people, without appearing to change. The institution will have accepted its residents when they have been rejected from everywhere else. It cannot be harmed no matter how angry or destructive its residents feel, and is thereby reassuring. In summary, the institution takes on the form of the 'good parent' that the institutionalised person either never had, or had and lost.

Therefore, when institutions close, or when we decide that the person must leave 'for their own good' we may not be surprised if we meet with resistance. Indeed, it will certainly be a very difficult task to help them become accustomed to life in their new world, be it adult foster home, group home, hostel, flat or Part 3 accommodation.

In their years in hospital, the institutionalised patient will have had everything done for him, meals prepared, shopping done, laundry attended to, medical check-ups automatically—even his tea already milked and sugared! Some severely institutionalised patients will have lost the capacity to speak and to move freely. In the total institution, one does not need to move, nor to ask for anything.

There are no clear guidelines for social work with this type of patient, since it is untested ground. Other countries have closed their mental hospitals, with varying degrees of after-care and success, the United States and Italy most recently. However, certain principles can be delineated, to provide a strategy from which to operate:

1. The most important principle must be that each social worker is able to work in the way in which he feels at ease. Anxiety transmits itself, and the work is demanding. We cannot go on for long in a situation where we ourselves feel uncomfortable.

2. The next step is to work with others as a team and for that team 'to

get its own house in order' as the priority. We cannot help others if we ourselves are in disarray. The pressures placed on us by our clients, by society and by our own professionalism are too great to be sustained without support from others who share our concerns.

3. Assess each person individually, shaping rehabilitation programmes towards individual needs and potentialities. The institutionalised patient—as is the case with the long-term mentally ill generally—is not a member of a homogeneous group. Each patient's capacities are different, each patient's personality unique. For one person, speaking his name may be a major step forward; for another, drawing a sketch may be a sign of psychic growth.

4. Avoid over-stimulating environments. Research has shown that even with the long-term institutionalised patient whose obvious signs of mental illness have disappeared (no more delusions, for example), if placed in an over-stimulating or stressful environment, his more florid symptoms will recur.

5. Do not expect or demand too much from the patient. Institutionalisation makes people into very withdrawn, passive and quiet individuals. Even intensive rehabilitation over a period of years may mean little outward change in their demeanour or behaviour.

6. Indefinite commitment: home is not a transient place. The clients will need to feel that what they have is theirs for good.

Placement

Placement for the institutionalised patient needs careful thought. It can only be decided when the patient has been assessed and given some opportunity to develop life skills (by this we mean cooking, cleaning, shopping, washing, etc.). Some may develop sufficiently to live in a bedsit or group home. We should not think of ourselves as failures, however, if the rehabilitation work shows that what the institutionalised, ex-patient wants and we might add, needs, is a place where he can continue to be looked after and cared for. This is what patients have been led to by their years in the total institution and it may be said that it is their right to have a similar setting in their old age. In this case an elderly person's home may be the most appropriate home for them.

THE 'NEW LONG STAY' MENTALLY ILL

The present population of mental hospitals consists, in the main, of patients who have been there for most of their adult lives, whose illnesses have been absorbed by the institution, and whose very personalities seem to have 'burnt out'. They can be described generically as the 'old long stay' mentally ill. As such they retain the secondary disability of institutionalisation: apathy, withdrawal, and mutism. With the closures of such institutions, these people will continue to need basic care. There is, however, another group of patients now recognised as the 'new long stay' mentally ill population.

The new long stay patients represent a younger group of people who have a long-term mental illness. As a group they have frequent, and recurring, mental hospital admissions, characterising the 'revolving door' syndrome. This group of people responds to consistency and continuity of care. They are especially vulnerable because they are unable to sustain a completely independent life in the community; but with the closures of formal institutions and the nationwide (indeed, international) rundown of services, may have nowhere to turn at times of crises.

Unlike the old long stay patients whose essential needs centre on basic care, the new long stay patients are active people, who make heavy demands on their carers, and the statutory services in general. Without sufficient resources, support, or commitment, these patients will be unable to manage when the total institution has disappeared. Society will then have on its hands a large population of drifting, homeless, uncared for, and mentally ill individuals.

REFERENCES AND FURTHER READING

Allederidge P. (1979). Hospitals, madhouses and asylums: cycles in the care of the insane. *Br. J. Psychiatry*; **134**: 321–34.

Barton R. (1966). *Institutional Neurosis*. Bristol: John Wright.

Berger P. L., Berger B., Kellner H. (1973). *The Homeless Mind*. London: Penguin.

Boffey P. M. (1984). US tragedy: the roving mentally ill. *International Herald Tribune*, 14 Sept.

Bowlby J. (1968). *Child Care and the Growth of Love*. London: Penguin.

Brandon D., Wells K., Francis C., Ramsey E. (1980). *The Survivors*. London: Routledge & Kegan Paul.

Caplan G., Killilea M. (1976). *Support Systems and Mutual Help*. New York: Grune & Stratton.

Cohen S., Taylor L. (1977). *Psychological Survival*. London: Penguin.

Cree W., Mann S. M. (1976). New long stay psychiatric patients 1972–3. *Psychological Med.*; **6**: 603–16.

Foucault M. (1971). *Madness and Civilization*. London: Tavistock Publications.

Glasscote R., ed. (1975). *The Alternate Service*. Washington DC: Joint Information Service.

Goffman E. (1976). *Asylum*. London: Pelican.

Goffman E. (1976). *Stigma*. London: Pelican.

Hinshelwood R. D., Manning N. (1979). *Therapeutic Communities*. London: Routledge & Kegan Paul.

Jahoda M., Lazarfield P. F., Zeisel H. (1972). *Merienthal: The Sociography of an Unemployed Community*. London: Tavistock Publications.

Jones C., Fowles A. J. (1984). *Ideas on Institutions*. London: Routledge & Kegan Paul.

Jones K., Poletti A. (1984). The mirage of a reform. *New Society*, 5 Oct.

Jones M. (1982). *The Process of Change*. London: International Library of Group Psychotherapy and Group Process.

Lamb H. R. (1982). *Treating the Long Term Mentally Ill*. London: Josey-Bass.

Long H. (1985). We want to be like everyone, not goldfish in a bowl. *Community Care*, 25 April.

Meacher M., ed. (1979). *New Methods of Mental Health Care*. Oxford: Pergamon.

Olsen M. R., ed. (1979). *The Care of the Mentally Disordered*. Birmingham: BASW.

Reed J., Lomas G. (1984). *Psychiatric Services in the Community*. London: Croom Helm.

Robins L. N., Clayton P. J., Wing J. K. (1980). *The Social Consequences of Psychiatric Illness*. New York: Brunner/Mazel.

Scull A. T. (1973). *Decarceration*. Englewood Cliffs, NJ: Spectrum.

Townsend P. (1979). *Poverty in the UK*. London: Penguin.

Wing J. K., Hailey A., eds. (1972). *Evaluating a Community Psychiatric Service*. Oxford: Oxford University Press.

Wing J. K., Olsen R. (1979). *Community Care for the Mentally Disabled*. Oxford: Oxford Medical Publications.

Winnicot D. W. (1982). The mentally ill in your caseload (1963). In *The Maturational Processes and the Facilitating Environment*. London: The Hogarth Press and Institute of Psychoanalysis.

Chapter 12

Aspects of Understanding: Client and Social Worker

TAKING CARE OF OURSELVES?

Social work makes extreme and intense demands on us as practitioners. Clients make us feel despair, anger, frustration, sadness, failure. How do we cope with these feelings? How do we take care of ourselves?

One way of taking care may be to do just that. Take care not to be too involved; to become rigidly professional; giving just enough and nothing more; taking longer holidays; going on lots of courses; limiting our client contact; reducing, or 'rationalising', office and duty hours. 'Burn out' is a common phenomenon amongst members of the caring professions and has received considerable attention because of its destructive nature.

The combined effect of these various factors is, in one way or another, to deprive the client of ourselves. This may be what some of our clients want. However, is there another way of taking care of ourselves so as not to collude with some of the more destructive forces in our work? Is there a way to understand these difficulties and enable us to feel nourished and creative in what we do?

We can view these processes structurally: see our difficulties in the light of our roles as members of a system. This is helpful, especially for workers in institutions. Another way may be to accept the feelings within us and use them as gateways to greater understanding. Used in this way, our feelings about our clients may act as communication rather than as hindrances.

PROJECTIVE IDENTIFICATION

A way of seeing client–social worker interacting in this manner exists most clearly in the psychoanalytic concept of projective identification.

As an experience, projective identification can be found described in the clinical work of Freud and Jung. It was first described as a workable concept by Melanie Klein in her paper, 'Notes on some Schizoid Mechanisms', in 1946. To understand this concept it is necessary to see feelings and emotions as parts of the self. They can be experienced unconsciously as either attacking and persecutory, or alternatively, rewarding and benevolent. Either of these sensations can be so overwhelming that instead of being able to accept that they belong to oneself, the theory of projective identification holds that the individual experiences the unconscious demand to project them out into someone else, locating the centre of anxiety externally rather than internally. These feelings are projected into others, but since they are nevertheless part of oneself, one still retains control over them, thus one is still identified with them. In this way, feelings become ways of manipulating other people unconsciously, other people become the bearer of one's own worst and best feelings.

Projective identification differs from projection in terms of degree. In projection, we may invest others with attributes and feelings that in reality are our own. In projective identification this becomes actually experienced by the other as an emotion inside them—something which may be quite strange to them and certainly difficult to control. Klein saw the origins of this process as lying in the earliest stages of infancy, where the infant's personality is disorganised and unintegrated, but liable to feel very powerful emotions. The infant puts these feelings into its mother in order to feel safe. It has two effects: the expulsion of 'bad things', and the creation of the sense of unconscious control over the mother. These mechanisms are then repeated in later life, in our relationships with others.

Thus, we as social workers feel despair because the clients cannot — they are permeated with despair but if they feel it at all, they would be overwhelmed by it. We feel anger at the client who feels inadequate and afraid, probably of his own anger. We fail the clients who are afraid of their failure. Like one of Laing's knots, the list and the variations are endless.

Case illustration

A clearer example may be an interview with the mother of a young schizophrenic man. He lives at home with his mother and father. His mother spends her time being worried and exhausted by her son. His father absents himself, wanting nothing to do with his son who he regards as a failure. The son spends his days either wandering the streets, or sleeping in bed till all hours. His illness takes the form of delusions about being persecuted and haunted. In this family there is a complex group process at work. The social worker experiences this in the form of helpless frustration occasioned by the schizophrenic's mother, which causes the social worker to flee the household in despair and exhaustion.

One dynamic that this incident highlights is the way in which the client's mother's concern is so strongly felt and expressed that it gets under the skin and inside the social worker; but instead of being experienced simply as concern, it is experienced by the social worker as a persecutory anguish. So much so that it is unbearable and the social worker must flee.

Looking at this experience in relation to the schizophrenic client himself, we see that he cannot bear too much involvement from any source. He is, and seems to wish to be, isolated. He wanders alone with no intimate friends, he frequently misses social work appointments. One way of viewing self-inflicted isolation is as a defence against being invaded and overwhelmed by such feelings as the social worker experienced. Paradoxically, however, and tragically, such isolation is recognised as psychic pain by the schizophrenic's mother, and causes her increased anguish and worry; thus causing a vicious cycle of worry, withdrawal and increased worry. It could even be added that the schizophrenic cannot totally evade such feelings. They often manifest themselves in haunting and persecutory delusions that make the schizophrenic firmly believe that the world is plainly out to invade, or even kill him.

VIOLENCE AND PROJECTIVE IDENTIFICATION

Violence proves to be another area where projective identification is carried out. The client who feels filled with inarticulate rage may crash into a social work office waving a knife or the approved social worker may be called to a situation where a person is 'out of control' waving knives and shouting abuse. The perfectly natural reaction is to feel fear; then the need for self-defence. We can act on each of these. We can run; or we can stand and fight. What may be being acted out, however, is a drama which originates within the client's own psyche. Thus if we feel fear, we may be being invaded by the frightened part of the client. The client is afraid of his own feelings—feelings which are so powerful that they seem to be violent. The consequent sense of panic is projected into others, including ourselves. We then in our turn become afraid, our judgement is clouded, leaving us liable to panic. It is at times such as this when our greatest asset is the ability to stay calm; sit down where the client is standing up, speak quietly where the client is shouting, not do very much where the client is expecting a war. Our ability not to panic, to contain and provide a limit to the client's sense of being out of control may be the reason why he has come to us.

These things said, the difficult balance to maintain, with regard to violence, is the need not to escalate a situation as against the need to protect oneself. The prime motive must always be to care for oneself and if we feel filled with dreadful and overpowering fear, then we are probably in a situation that is too much for us to handle. We should then have no qualms about either getting out of it—by running—or getting to help as quickly as we safely can.

PROJECTIVE IDENTIFICATION AND ORGANISATIONS

Projective identification can also be found operating between clients and organisations, within organisations, and between one organisation and another. An example would be the client who goes from one social work agency to another, using different names, cross-referring problems, or criticising other workers in their absence. A complex chain of intra-agency knots can be tied. These will defeat the agencies concerned, but also confirm the client's own negative self-image. The client has put into the respective agencies parts of himself, so that the agencies and their social workers act out the conflicts that the client normally feels internally. This can give the client some relief from the demands of his illness.

SOCIAL WORK AND PROJECTIVE IDENTIFICATION

The importance of the concept of projective identification for social workers is two-fold.

Firstly, if the unconscious motivation for projective identification is to control and distance the other person, then being aware of the process may act as a defence against being manipulated into acting against one's judgement or inclination. Being forced to act against one's judgement and inclination is often the situation that social workers find themselves put into by both their clients and also other agencies. We should keep in mind the fact that in any situation, but especially ones where the protagonists have a strong emotional investment, there will be strong unconscious forces at work. Forces which, by definition, we may know nothing about. Then we, at least, may be on our guard, and can aim to know our own minds.

This leads on to the second importance of the concept, which is to help us understand what, on the surface, will certainly seem to be very complex and mysterious events. This may not help us to change these events. The events will have a life of their own and we as social workers will be coming on to the scene very late in the day. But understanding our own predicament when faced with these baffling events may give us clues as to what, at least, we ought not to do.

We may be talking about what seems to be an impossible task. Being aware of projective identification does not imply a sense of omniscience in the social worker, far from it. When we experience a sense of omniscience, we are more than likely to be in a process whereby the client, or his situation, has entered into us in such a way as to put into us all the possible feelings of goodness and benevolence which he himself finds too powerfully overwhelming to bear. The client feels small, inadequate, and ignorant. We are the ones with insight and knowledge.

Thus, we can see that being aware of the process of projective identification implies far more than a desire for omniscience: it implies a readiness to accept the mystery of a situation and a client, and to let these become part of oneself. Listening to and feeling the responses in oneself then gives one messages as to what it is that the client is experiencing.

A third aspect of projective identification for social workers thus emerges in the way in which it ascribes to us the role of caretaker. To be a caretaker for the most damaged, or damaging, aspects of our clients. We carry for our clients their despair, their failure, their anger—and sometimes their goodness, their achievements. If we can contain these feelings and gradually, through the mediation of effective counselling and casework, hand them back in a non-punitive but accepting way, then we will be able to help our clients come to some clearer understanding of themselves and their predicaments. By helping them to integrate these unacknowledged and unwanted parts of their selves, we may help our clients gain more in integrity, self-respect and power.

Projective identification, therefore, carries a resource for us as social workers. It can make sense of some of the baffling, and despairing situations that we encounter, and which no matter what we do, 'get inside us'. It can help us keep our feet on the ground when all about us are losing their heads and more often than not, blaming it on us. It can help us to help the clients make more sense of their lives and themselves.

It does carry with it a price, however, which is that to make full use of our feelings and intuition, we must become and remain open and sensitive to ourselves. This can be seen conversely in the situation where, because of a blind spot in ourselves, we continually meet up with the same difficulty repeated in the lives of our clients; or in a similar way we unconsciously are drawn to those clients who most nearly represent our own internal needs.

Examples of this could be the social worker who is repeatedly experiencing violence in the course of his work; the social worker who often finds himself falling in love with his clients; the social worker who cannot say no; the social worker who says no too readily; the social worker whose clients are always teetering on the brink of breakdown (and need their social worker to keep them there).

If the client projectively identifies into us, we may in our turn, projectively identify into the client. This can create difficulties for the progress of our work, unless properly understood and dealt with by the social worker, through whatever means he finds most helpful. These can be many and various, but can range from supervision, to team work, to consultation, and perhaps, psychotherapy or analysis for himself.

REFERENCES AND FURTHER READING

Fordham M., Gordon R., Hubback J., Lambert K., eds. (1979). *Technique in Jungian Analysis*. London: William Heinemann.

Freud S. (1975). Group psychology and the analysis of the ego. In *Complete Works of S. Freud, Volume 18*. London: Hogarth Press.

Jung C. G. (1976). The practice of psychotherapy. In *Collected Works, Volume 16*. London: Routledge & Kegan Paul.

Klein M. (1980). Notes on some schizoid mechanisms. In *Envy and Gratitude and Other Works, 1946–63*. London: Hogarth Press and Institute of Psychoanalysis.

Laing R. D. (1973). *Knots*. London: Penguin.

Segal H. (1981). *Introduction to the Work of Melanie Klein*. London: Hogarth Press.

Steiner J. (1982). Personal psychotherapy in the training of a psychiatrist. *Bull. R. Coll. Psychiatrists*; **March**: 41.

Part II

Social work practice and legislation

Chapter 13
Care or Control?

Modern sociological theory has questioned the role of the 'helping professions' in general, and of psychiatry and social work in particular. Ssasz has written of the 'Myth of Mental Illness' and the 'Manufacture of Madness'; Illich has discussed the 'Disabling Profession'; North has described social workers and counsellors as 'Secular Priests' enforcing a new religion on their unwitting and vulnerable clients; Halmos has written of the 'Faith of the Counsellors'. In the UK the psychiatric profession has had its own radicals, beginning with Laing and Cooper, who were the leading lights of the anti-psychiatry movement. Recently Wood has written on the 'Myth of Neurosis'.

There are many theoretical strands to these ideas. They are not homogeneous. They are not of one political ideology. The question which they point to is very much alive and real in the day to day work of social work in relation to mental health: to invoke a Section under the Mental Health Act 1983 is to remove a person's liberty and to define him as a 'mental patient'. To do so without being aware of the ethical and practical implications may be to be colluding with a coercive and anti-therapeutic process. To 'section' someone is not a responsibility to be undertaken lightly, but not to undertake it at all may be more detrimental to an individual's well-being. For example, the Psichiatrica Democratica movement in Italy has produced a situation where compulsorily to detain someone suspected of being mentally ill, the signature of a judge and a doctor is required—not a social worker. This bears a close resemblance to the situation in Victorian England where the signature of a magistrate was the requisite authority to detain someone in a mental hospital.

Social workers are trained to assess and understand the moral and psycho-social implications of a compulsory admission. To ignore this fact may well be to leave the responsibility for hospital admissions under the 1983 Act to the police (under Section 136) or the other arms of the judicial process. Zumpe, writing in the Guardian (1984) has indicated the ways in which police and court powers are being used increasingly often in the circumstances of mentally ill individuals; by remands and powers under Part III of the Mental Health Act 1983. Indeed, the Act makes it a requirement in law for social workers to look for the 'least restrictive environment' for therapeutic care. Therefore the liberty principle is recognised under the Act. But going further, how can we as professionals interested not only in the liberty but also the care of those suffering from a mental illness reconcile what may seem to be conflicting principles?

There are two important aspects to this question, which unite these opposing principles. The first is to do with structure; the second, with the nature of mental illness itself.

STRUCTURE

Compulsory admission to hospital is a restriction of the individual's liberty. But it is also a way of introducing structure into what may be a frightening and chaotic situation in which the client finds himself. Without some kind of structure any setting can be restrictive. Structure provides a kind of freedom so that we know where we are, what our aims can be; and what expectations there are upon us. Structure affords a basis for choice. Linking into the issue of structure, is the question of mental illness.

MENTAL ILLNESS

Throughout all the clinical symptoms, and classifications of illness, there seem to be three essential features of mental illness:

1. The distressing experience of it for the sufferer.
2. The out-of-control nature of the sufferer's behaviour.
3. The difficulty society has in accepting the sufferer's possibly bizarre behaviour.

The invocation of a compulsory order, and the admission to a hospital can provide an accepting community of professionals, which contains the sufferer's distress, and enables treatment to be administered which will alleviate the distress.

Structure needs to be used therapeutically, not punitively. But when a person is in the throes of a mental illness, they are not 'of themselves'; they often cannot decide what is in their best interests. Becoming mentally ill is one way of relinquishing responsibility, including the responsibility to one's self—hence the self-neglect, starvation, and homelessness of many seriously mentally ill individuals.

APPLICATION

The application to the managers of a mental hospital is made by a social worker on the recommendation of the medical practitioner(s). The responsibility for such a decision, therefore, clearly rests on the social worker.

OBJECTIONS TO COMPULSORY ADMISSION

These are related to the sociological, historical, and political perspectives contained in the writings of the authors quoted above. They centre firstly on theoretical objections—to do with the power and secrecy of the medical professions; the professionalisation, and therefore exclusivity, increasingly adopted by the 'helping professions' (including social work); and the mystique of knowledge.

Secondly, objections centre on practical issues; colluding with a family pathology which locates all the family's disturbances in one person, the 'identified patient'; stigmatising a person and giving him the status of a prisoner; exposing a vulnerable person to the vicissitudes of institutionalisation where, stripped of responsibility, he quickly loses the ability to be responsible.

Let us examine some of these complex issues in practice.

CASE ILLUSTRATIONS

An assessment for compulsory admission

Our first example is a woman, who has a long and often repeated history of mental hospital admission, followed by discharge to hostels (hostel dwelling was her expressed preference), followed by failure to attend out-patient clinics, failure to take medication and active resistance to any form of ongoing social work support. She has been living in her present hostel accommodation for several months and, as in countless previous instances, begins to claim that the hostel staff are taking her money and plotting against her. She has had to leave several hostels in the past because they could not tolerate her persecuted feelings, which generate in her a sense of bitter isolation (in practice she eventually begins to abuse the staff, and refuses to pay her rent). Hostel placements have become increasingly difficult to obtain because, after each breakdown, hostels have refused to have her return as a resident. The staff of the hostel contact the client's social worker and inform him that they are worried about her. She has become increasingly isolated and angry; she claims that the hostel staff are stealing her money and molesting her during the night. The social worker visits and makes his assessment of the client, in conjunction with her GP. They decide that she is clearly in a vulnerable state: she has stopped and refuses even to consider taking any medication. She is expressing paranoid ideas, but wants to deal with her difficulties herself without 'interference'.

Should the social worker and GP proceed to apply for a compulsory hospital admission in order to prevent a complete breakdown of both the client and the placement; or should they, in the interests of liberty, allow the client to continue without statutory intervention? In this case, the client was not compulsorily admitted to hospital. It was felt by the GP and social worker that she had a place to live that could at that time contain her; that she was adamantly insisting on her rights to stay where she was and that, at the time of assessment, she could manage without any help. Furthermore, it was considered potentially anti-therapeutic to invoke a Section as, in this client's case, it may have destroyed the last vestiges of trust she still had in the social worker.

Neither the GP nor the social worker were certain that their decision was the correct one, although each agreed upon it. They felt that it was a risk, but a risk that needed to be taken in the interests of the patient's liberty, her own wishes, and their judgement about their own therapeutic relationship with her. The GP and social worker, in fact, wondered whether it might not have been more appropriate to have admitted the woman compulsorily to a mental hospital, in order to stabilise her on medication.

Somewhat to their surprise, however, the client remained stable for several months following their assessment. She did eventually relapse, was evicted from her hostel place, and brought into mental hospital by the police under Section 136. At that moment in time, the caring services had not been involved in the process of her eviction. In the light of the length of her stay outside of hospital, it seemed to the GP and social worker that their earlier decision had been correct. It seemed to have been worth the risk, in view of her ability to remain stable in the community in the subsequent months.

In consideration of guardianship

A middle aged man has a long history of institutional care, dating back to early infancy, when his mother died. His spells in institutions have been punctuated by intervals when he has lived in the community. On these occasions he has preferred to live the life of a vagrant. He enjoys sleeping rough. He believes that when he does, something 'exciting' might happen to him. But the only thing that happens is that he neglects himself to the point of emaciation and infestation; so that at worst he is brought into casualty units in a state of near death. At best, he is quickly transferred to psychiatric wards with a diagnosis of schizophrenia and detained under a Section. He now wishes to be discharged from hospital. A group home has been found for him by the social worker, to which the patient agrees to go, whilst still under his Section. He makes no secret of the fact that if discharged he would go and live rough again.

Should guardianship be invoked so that he can be asked to live where the local authority feels is most beneficial? Is this an infringement of his liberty and should he be discharged to be brought in again as a casualty case when necessary? Should he be allowed to neglect himself, and his mental condition deteriorate, so as to put his physical health at risk to the point of death? In this case, with the patient's grudging consent, guardianship was invoked under Section 7 of the 1983 Act. He moved into the group home, with daily attendance at a day centre. There were no more episodes of his becoming a vagrant. In this situation, it seemed to the social worker involved that guardianship made a major contribution to actually keeping his client out of total institutional care.

COMMENT

There are clearly no easy answers to these difficult decisions. They do however reveal the depth of responsibility of the social work role. Responsibility may be used responsibly; or it can be abdicated from. The decisions made must ultimately be in the light of our professional judgement, ethical commitment and perhaps most important, our concern for our client's well-being.

SELF-DETERMINATION

Client self-determination is the underlying principle behind most social work intervention. But this can only take place where the client is neither confused nor persecuted by the vicissitudes of his mental illness. The client who has given up control of his own life is not able to take a clear or considered decision about his wishes and needs for the future. His judgement on these matters will be impaired or obliterated.

If we take the second example given above, the person who chooses to live rough may be making a decision based on considered judgement. But when he does so for delusional reasons and when he is neglecting himself to the point where his resources are becoming exhausted, we may be justified in intervening to enable him to regain control of his own life.

OTHER CONSIDERATIONS

Of equal relevance, but beyond the scope of our present text, care and control questions are raised in several other areas of social work practice: such as child care (for example, the extent of social services' responsibility in monitoring children at risk, as against a family's right to privacy and self-determination); adolescence (the adolescent's need for boundaries as against their desire for independence); the elderly (the right to medical treatment as against the right to die 'with dignity').

REFERENCES AND FURTHER READING

Bailey R., Brake M., eds. (1975). *Radical Social Work*. Leeds: E. J. Arnold.

Biestek F. (1973). *The Casework Relationship*. London: Unwin University Books.

Blackburn R., ed. (1978). *Ideology in Social Science*. London: Fontana.

Brandon D. (1976). *Zen in the Art of Helping*. London: Routledge & Kegan Paul.

Cooper D. (1967). *Psychiatry and Anti-Psychiatry*. London: Tavistock Publications.

Fletcher J. (1966). *Situation Ethics*. London: SCM Press.

Fromm E. (1961). *The Art of Loving*. London: Allen & Unwin.

George V., Wilding P. (1976). *Ideology and Social Welfare*. London: Routledge & Kegan Paul.

Halmos P. (1965). *The Faith or the Counsellors*. London: Hutchinson.

Illich I. (1977). *Disabling Professions*. London: Marion Boyars.

Laing R. D. (1975). *The Politics of Experience and the Bird of Paradise*. London: Penguin.

Murdoch I. (1970). *The Sovereignty of Good*. London: Routledge & Kegan Paul.

National Deviancy Conference/Conference on Socialist Economics (1979). *Capitalism and the Rule of Law*. London: Hutchinson.

North M. (1972). *The Secular Priests*. London: Allen & Unwin.

North M. (1975). *The Mind Market*. London: Allen & Unwin.

Pearce F. (1978). *Crimes of the Powerful*. London: Pluto.

Plant R. (1970). *Social and Moral Theory in Casework*. London: Routledge & Kegan Paul.

Smart C., Smart B., eds. (1978). *Women, Sexuality, and Social Control*. London: Routledge & Kegan Paul.

Ssasz T. (1962). *The Myth of Mental Illness*. London: Secker & Warburg.

Ssasz T. (1971). *The Manufacture of Madness*. London: Routledge & Kegan Paul.

Ssasz T. (1977). *The Theology of Medicine*. Baton Rouge: Louisiana State University.

Statham D. (1978). *Radicals in Social Work*. London: Routledge & Kegan Paul.

Storr A. (1974). *The Integrity of the Personality*. London: Penguin.

Tillich P. (1970). *The Courage to Be*. London: Fontana.

Wilson M. (1975). *Health is for People*. London: Darton, Longman & Todd.

Zumpe K. (1984). The mad world of the Mental Health Act. *The Guardian*, 12 Dec.

Chapter 14

Assessment

'Before making an application for the admission of a patient to hospital the Approved Social Worker shall interview the patient in a suitable manner and satisfy himself that detention in a hospital is in all the circumstances of the case the most appropriate way of providing the care and medical treatment of which the patient stands in need.'

Section 13(2) Mental Health Act 1983

The request for an approved social worker to visit indicates that someone is worried and/or is seeking immediate action. Referrals for an approved social worker to assess for admission to hospital often come from GPs but may also come from relatives, neighbours, friends, other social workers or from community nurses. In fact, anyone who is concerned about the mental health of someone else may contact a local authority social services department for help or advice.

In the case of a nearest relative requesting an application for admission to hospital the approved social worker has a duty (Section 13(4)) under the Mental Health Act to consider the case as soon as it is practicable and if an application for admission to hospital is not made the reasons must be recorded in a case file to be kept by the social services department. The nearest relative has to be informed of the reasons in writing.

Whoever is requesting action, the approved social worker is called upon to be able to recognise and respond to people under stress and help them to focus on what the problem is and what can realistically be done to ease the situation, which is concerning them. There are as many methods of assessment as there are individual social workers; and more important than following one method is perhaps to develop one's own style and feel happy with it. However, there are basic principles which can be delineated, and one strategy incorporating these is given below.

INITIAL CONTACT

Note the name and telephone number of the referrer. Ascertain their relationship to the person being referred. Find out exactly who they are concerned about and where that person lives. It is a requirement of the Act that if the referrer is the GP, he should have seen his patient within the past 24 hours if he is recommending compulsory admission to hospital under the Mental Health Act.

RESPONSIBILITY FOR ACTION

The Mental Health Act makes it clear that it is the duty of an approved social worker to make an application in respect of a patient within the area of the social services authority by whom he is appointed (Section 13(2)). However, an application for admission for assessment may be made by an approved social worker outside the area of the local social services authority by which he is appointed (Section 13(3)). This is a new provision of the 1983 Act and it enables an approved social worker who is already working with a client to make an assessment for compulsory admission wherever that client happens to be. Nevertheless, it is undoubtedly good practice to establish geographical location, together with an automatic check to discover whether a client (or referrer) is known to the department. Much unnecessary effort on the part of all concerned can be avoided in this way.

WORK WITH THE REFERRER

The approved social worker needs to be able to get as complete a picture as possible of the present situation in order to judge the degree of urgency. There must be some significance in the timing of the referral and this needs to be discussed with the referrer and understood by the social worker. The approved social worker needs to explain to the referrer the grounds for making a compulsory admission to hospital:

1. That the patient is suffering from mental disorder of a nature or degree that warrants his detention in a hospital for assessment (or for assessment followed by medical treatment) for at least a limited period.
2. That he ought to be so detained in the interests of his own health or safety or with a view to the protection of other persons (Section 2(2)). However, even if it is apparent that there is no threat involved, the approved social worker should be responsive to all requests for help concerning someone thought to be mentally disordered and at risk. If there is no urgency, the approved social worker should take a referral, as for any other client referred to the

department, and arrange to see the referrer and/or client or pass the referral to the appropriate area social worker.

The referrer can be asked to talk about what is happening to the patient at this precise moment in time. Where is the client? Is he or she alone? What is it that is worrying the referrer? Is the client aware of the referral and the reasons for concern?

These are some of the questions the social worker will need to answer. The social worker will be sensitive to the fact that the referrer may well be under considerable stress and, at this stage, the taking of a detailed family history would not be helpful. The focus at the initial stage has to be on the degree of urgency and an assessment as to the appropriate immediate intervention needed to relieve the anxiety of the referrer and help the patient. The social worker needs to talk clearly and simply, be patient and to listen to the referrer. If there is anything that is not clear the social worker must clarify this with the referrer. The social worker will also ensure that the referrer understands what action the worker is going to take, how long this will take and who will be involved. The referrer or the person referred may have a communication problem, and it would be well to ascertain if this is the case, in advance. Obviously, language problems are important but there are also cultural factors relating to patients from ethnic minorities. For example, the acceptability of a male doctor or social worker to a female Muslim patient. The social worker should discuss this with the referrer as it may be essential to ensure that an interpreter or other members of the family are present at the interview.

The approved social worker may wish to have available lists of local language interpreters and lists of workers for the deaf and dumb. Some knowledge of local ethnic minorities may also be valuable.

ACCESS

There may be problems about how the social worker will get in to see the client. The social worker needs to clarify this with the referrer and ask if there will be someone at the house to open the door and also if there is anyone else who knows the person referred, such as a home help, psychiatric nurse, priest, good neighbour, friend or relative. This information will be crucial if the client refuses to open the door and it is necessary to involve someone he knows and trusts.

PREPARATION FOR ASSESSMENT VISIT

The GP must always be contacted immediately following a referral and informed of the reasons for concern. Some GPs may be reluctant to do a joint assessment visit with the approved social worker, particularly if they have recently seen the client. However, it is helpful to the client for the GP and the social worker to visit together as they will be able to suggest alternatives to hospital care, i.e. out-patient clinic, day hospital, community psychiatric nursing, environmental changes. If there is no known GP, the approved social worker should have available a list of approved doctors known to the social services department and should contact someone on the list to make a joint assessment visit.

VENUE

This is usually where the patient is at the time of the referral. Access arrangements will have been clarified with the referrer. However, the client may refuse to open the door or to come out of the bedroom or lavatory.

> 'An Approved Social Worker of a local Social Services Authority may at all reasonable times after producing, if asked to do so, some duly authenticated document showing that he is such a Social Worker, enter and inspect any premises (not being a hospital) in the area of that authority in which a mentally disordered patient is living, if he has reasonable cause to believe that the patient is not under proper care.'
>
> *Section 115 Mental Health Act 1983*

If it is impossible to gain access to the house or to a room where the client is believed to be, without forcing an entry, the social worker has to obtain a warrant authorising the police to force entry and, if necessary, to remove the client to a 'place of safety' with a view to making an assessment and application for admission, or other alternative arrangements for treatment or care. In order to obtain a warrant the social worker has to go to a Justice of the Peace and give information, under oath, as to the reasons for concern (Section 135(1)).

A named police constable is then empowered to force entry and remove the client if requested by an approved social worker who has obtained a warrant. The policeman and approved social worker should be accompanied by a registered medical practitioner.

DOCUMENTS AND INFORMATION

Whatever the outcome of an assessment interview, the approved social worker should not put himself in the position of having to rush out looking for a telephone or to collect a supply a documents. Ideally, he should have a documents 'kit' to take to any assessment interview. This should include:

Application for Admission Form.
Medical Recommendations Form.
Personal identification documents.
A leaflet giving details of the patient's rights if admitted to hospital.
Handbook of services available to the mentally ill and relevant application forms.
List of community resources, voluntary organisations, animal care, religious organisations, counselling services.
Child care information and forms for reception into care, nurseries, child minders.
Details of home care services.

AVAILABILITY OF HOSPITAL BED

The approved social worker will need to know if there is a hospital bed available if needed. The GP has the responsibility to find a hospital bed and this can always be provisionally reserved by the GP to be available if needed. The normal way for anyone to go into hospital in an emergency is by ambulance and the mentally ill person should not be regarded differently.

USE OF POLICE

The social worker has to consider whether or not to involve the police from the beginning. This is a difficult decision and can only be decided in the light of what is known about the previous history of the client and what is happening now.

Case illustration
A woman who had been in hospital several times with diagnoses of schizophrenia begins to break up her furniture and throw the pieces through the window of her flat with considerable force, regardless of neighbours or passers-by. She has a small axe and is refusing to open the door to anyone. Only when the police arrive and firmly ask her to open the door does she do this. The police quickly take the axe from her. It is then possible and safe for the approved social worker and GP to assess how best to help her. After hours of drama it was only when the police arrived that the woman calmed down. In such situations the

help of the police can diminish further upset rather than increase what is already an explosive situation.

The police can be alerted of a worrying situation so that, if necessary, they can send someone along quickly. Approved social workers may be able to build up a relationship with their local police, which can save time and energy when a crisis involving the police occurs.

ASSESSMENT INTERVIEW

Assessment interviews with a view to deciding if compulsory admission to hospital is needed are often fraught. The social worker cannot know what he might find and the unexpected is always around the corner. The situation is often charged with anxiety and violence and there will be pressure on the social worker from relatives, doctor, police, or neighbours to 'do something'. This usually means getting rid of the 'problem' quickly! It is worth remembering that by the time a situation has reached the point of calling for an assessment for hospital admission there have probably been days, or weeks, of frightening behaviour and everyone is feeling the stress. Now the problem cannot be tolerated any longer and action is being demanded. Often the social worker will be going in 'cold' without having met any of the people involved in the crisis, including the other professionals.

STRUCTURE

A structured approach to an assessment interview can help. It brings a sense of order and clarity and enables those present to feel contained and held. When people are under stress they may not hear what is being said, may easily misunderstand and become angry or defensive. The social worker should be conscious of this throughout the interview and attempt to reduce tension by speaking simply, making sure everyone understands what is being said and having an unhurried but firm approach. All social workers will, of course, have their own individual style of working. However, a basic principle is to try to talk to the client, and family, as adult to adult without denying the regression they may be experiencing and help them to talk to each other. When people are in a disturbed emotional state they may find it difficult to function as adults and feel very powerless. The assessment interview is a crisis and could be a turning point both for the client and the family. It is important to involve them as actively as possible in the assessment, for instance, asking them to talk to each other. 'Can you tell your husband what it is that is upsetting you?' or 'Your wife tells me that she thinks you need to go into hospital. Could you perhaps tell her, and all of us, what you think about that?' Often when people feel desperate and at the end of their tether they no longer feel that they have any strength left to solve the problem. They may perceive the social worker and doctor as having great power, far beyond that of admitting someone to hospital for assessment.

Case illustration

The husband of an apparently paranoid woman rushed into another room when the social worker and doctor arrived. He felt powerless to deal with the situation and needed to be encouraged to take part in the interview. To exclude him could have served to emphasise his powerlessness whereas he perhaps could play a vital and enabling part in his wife's treatment and recovery.

There are many different models of crisis intervention services which are available. However, we need not forget that the origin of the word 'crisis' is 'turning point': it brings opportunities for change. The assessment interview might be seen not simply as a way of deciding whether or not someone needs to go into hospital, but also as the beginning of help for the client and family.

PRESENTING PROBLEM

This must be clear to the social worker and everyone involved before arranging the assessment interview.

Case illustration

A 20-year-old student has been sitting on her bed staring out of the window for days. She has not spoken or dressed herself and her flat mates are becoming extremely anxious because she is not eating and they fear that she might jump out of the window.

When the referrer is closely involved with the client, i.e. a family member or house sharer, he should be encouraged to participate in the assessment interview or, if he doesn't, the reasons for non-participation should be understood by the social worker and explained to the client at the start of the interview. It may help if the client is told at the beginning of the interview exactly who everyone present is, and why they are there. The most important task is then to invite the client to state the problem as he perceives it. Simple and direct questions should be asked, such as 'A lot of people are concerned about you (or: your friends are worried . . .) I'd like to hear from you what has been happening'. It is also important to ask the client if he understands why the social worker and doctor have come to see him.

ENGAGING WITH CLIENT

Every picture tells a story and everything that happens during the assessment interview will help the social worker to put together a picture of the client and assess the extent of the problem. His initial responses, the state of the surroundings and his ability to put into words what he thinks has been happening will form the basis of helping to resolve the problem. The social worker must be sensitive to the attitudes of everyone involved in the assessment and their effects on the client.

For example, when the husband rushed into another room in the *Case illustration* above, the social worker should notice the effect of this on the wife, draw her attention to her husband's absence and try to get her to help bring him back into the room, or say why she prefers him to remain outside.

Of course, there are some clients who are clearly too disturbed to be able to engage with the social worker. In such cases, it will be necessary to try to understand what 'normal' behaviour is like. The client may be in a florid disturbed state and what he says may not make any immediate sense at all. The social worker should not pretend that he understands the incomprehensible. He may be met with a confused and confusing person with very bizarre beliefs and only experience will help the social worker to develop the capacity to recognise and respond to the sane parts amongst so much disorder.

At the other extreme, the client might be making no response at all. Once again, the social worker needs to discover the significance of this and to talk to someone who knows the client. It is important not to presume that an unresponsive client is out of touch with what is going on, merely because he makes no verbal or visual contact. Even when someone is suffering from acute catatonic schizophrenia and appears to be completely mute and withdrawn he will be aware of what is going on and will be able to remember what happened.

Silence can be worked with and the social worker, using a gentle but confrontative approach, should challenge the silence: 'I want to try to understand what is worrying you but it is impossible if you won't talk to me'. If attempts to engage a response from a silent client have no apparent effect it is not helpful to continue. The social worker should then tell the client that in order to help him the social worker will have to consider calling in someone who knows him. If the client does not want this to happen he should be asked to indicate his objection.

For example the student who had not spoken for days in the *Case illustration* above made no response to the social worker, doctor or her friends. After a number of attempts to encourage her to talk about what was upsetting her the social worker said: 'It seems you will not speak to me or to your friends. We can't understand why you are doing this but we want to help you. Something must have upset you because only last week I understand you were at college and talking happily to your friends about your holiday plans. We decided we must telephone your parents as they will be concerned about you and will want to know what has happened. Please tell me if you do not want me to phone otherwise I will go ahead'.

There is no doubt that one potentially difficult type of client to engage with is the paranoid person who may interpret any approach with suspicion. With such a person it is very important to attempt to diminish their need to act out their hostility and to allow them to verbalise their fears.

If the client is threatening and aggressive then the social worker must take this seriously. In extreme cases the social worker should not deny the danger of the situation to himself and others involved. It may be necessary, and helpful, to involve the police where there is a real risk of actual assault. This is especially true where there has been a history of violence.

In order to make an assessment and look at alternatives the social worker has to try to make the situation feel safe for the client and everyone else involved. For instance, it can be helpful to alter the defensive stance of a threatening situation by simply suggesting that everyone should sit down and talk together and introducing normalising activities which should be implicit in our tone of voice and attitude to the client.

PSYCHO-SOCIAL FACTORS

When an approved social worker is called into an assessment situation he will be meeting a client, and often a family, in distress. The degree of this needs to be understood by knowing something about the way they have coped with stressful situations in the past. It may be that the boundaries between the client's internal and external world have temporarily broken down. If this is the case, what are the forces that have temporarily broken it down? What are the forces that have produced this situation and why have things gone so wrong at this point in time? These diagnostic links will help the worker to form a basis for an assessment which will help to make a realistic treatment plan.

Psychological factors which mainly concern the social worker are the client's ability to test out reality even when he is in the grips of a regression. Clearly it is not possible in one meeting to make an accurate measurement of the client's capacity to cope with the perennial problem of managing stress, but the worker must begin to forge a working relationship by identifying the problem which the client feels is most urgent and the ways he thinks he could be helped to make changes in his life.

There are often external social pressures which may have brought about the crisis and these experiences generally relate to loss, change and the ability to cope with the demands and expectations of other people. These stresses include:

1. Bereavement.
2. Life events:
    (a) Adolescence.
    (b) Marriage/divorce.
    (c) New relationships.
    (d) Pregnancy/parenthood.
    (e) Mid-life crisis.
    (f) Children leaving home.
    (g) Anniversaries.
3. Environmental changes (moving house, friends moving away).
4. Financial difficulties.
5. Status changes:
    (a) Promotion.
    (b) Change of job.
    (c) Redundancy/unemployment.
    (d) Retirement.
6. Illness.
7. Cultural and religious influences.
8. Role reversal.
9. Academic pressures.
10. Sexuality.
11. Drugs/alcohol.

CULTURAL FACTORS

In a mixed society such as ours the social worker needs to be very aware of the additional stresses experienced by clients from ethnic minorities and the added problems of communication, understanding of roles and attitudes to authority, see Chapter 8.

HISTORY

The client and family should be asked to tell the social worker what they feel are important factors in the past which have something to do with the present difficulties. They should also be asked about what and who they found helpful. The doctor and community psychiatric nurse will be able to provide medical history and to give information about recent changes in the client. The social worker must ask for their guidance as to any recent changes in medical and nursing management and the effects of any medication the client may be taking. A default in the pattern of medication invariably leads to a relapse and this can often be the primary reason for the client's present crisis.

This is particularly important in the case of patients with a history of schizophrenia who are on regular medication. An understanding of why the client has stopped medication and his fears about continuing should be discussed with the client and his family; and shared with the doctor and nurse.

DECISION ON ACTION

The formulation of a decision on action will have to draw together the risk factors, the range of options and the client's motivation. When the social worker has been called in with a view to compulsory admission under The Mental Health Act the risk factor is central to the assessment process. The social worker has to decide if the patient ought to be detained in hospital, 'in the interests of his *own* health or safety or with a view to the protection of *other persons*' (Section 2(2)(b)).

A mentally ill person who is destructive, either to people or property, as a result of hallucinations and delusions, is clearly recognisable as being a danger. However, the suicidal person is much less easy to recognise and the degree of his depression will determine the level of risk. It is wise to use a direct approach, take time to talk to the client and ask if he has considered ending his life, the subject of suicide should not be avoided. A depressed person who is alone is particularly vulnerable, see Chapter 4.

Mentally ill people, like those who are physically ill, need effective help and treatment if they are not to deteriorate. The approved social worker needs to be aware of the person who has become so fragmented that he is alienated from any good things within himself or from outside. He may need medical help but very often he is seen as a social problem. His chronic mental disorder may go unnoticed and he may not be offered treatment. Most social workers will be familiar with the client who neglects himself, appears dilapidated, lives in a world of his own and talks to himself and smiles at secret triumphs. This client needs medical help and should be referred for assessment as he may be seriously mentally ill and likely to deteriorate if not given treatment. His 'welfare' may be much more at risk than the obviously violent or acting out person.

The approved social worker has a responsibility to apply for admission if he is satisfied that the client is at risk and hospitalisation is the most appropriate way of providing the care and medical treatment he needs. A decision can only be made following an assessment of what is happening, the right of the client to be treated as an individual and offered alternatives to hospital care and, most importantly, the client's likelihood of accepting whatever help is available.

REFERENCES AND FURTHER READING

For references in the areas of social work and/or psychiatry readers are referred to material contained in Part I of the present text. Since most of the legislative matters contained in Part II are derived from overlapping sources, a unified reference list relating to legislation discussed in Chapters 14–19 can be found at the end of Chapter 19.

It should be noted that the legal powers described in the following pages refer to the legislative position in England and Wales, not that in Scotland or Northern Ireland.

Chapter 15

The Mental Health Act 1983: The Sections

As a general guide to The Mental Health Act 1983 we set out in this chapter all the sections in the order in which they appear within the Act. In subsequent chapters, we shall examine those sections of the 1983 Act which social workers are most likely to encounter in their practice. We will also highlight those aspects of other legislation which affect the social worker's role in the area of mental health.

In understanding and applying The Mental Health Act 1983, it is important also to make reference to the Mental Health (Hospital, Guardianship and Consent to Treatment) Regulations 1983. These, in several instances, amend or add to the provisions of the Act. The main provisions of the Act and Regulations are set out together in the DHSS Memorandum (1983).

THE MENTAL HEALTH ACT 1983

PART I
APPLICATION OF ACT

Section
1 Application of Act: 'mental disorder'.

PART II
COMPULSORY ADMISSION TO
HOSPITAL AND GUARDIANSHIP

Procedure for hospital admission

2. Admission for assessment.
3. Admission for treatment.
4. Admission for assessment in cases of emergency.
5. Application in respect of patient already in hospital.
6. Effect of application for admission.

Section

Section

Section

Section

Section

Supplemental

SCHEDULES

Chapter 16
Compulsory Powers

In this chapter we set out the main provisions of The Mental Health Act 1983 concerning compulsory hospital admission as relating to social workers. Other powers, such as doctors' and nurses' holding powers (Section 5) are discussed briefly, as are arrangements for patients concerned in criminal proceedings.

EMERGENCY (SECTION 4)

An example of the use of this section could be where an approved social worker is called in by a police doctor at 3 a.m. to assess a person who had approached their neighbour for 'supplies'. The neighbour was worried and called in the police. In the assessment it appears that the person is planning to drive to Egypt immediately without stopping. He has a car, but no licence; he believes himself to be invulnerable, i.e. will not be stopping at traffic lights. The GP is not known and the district psychiatric hospital is some 20 miles away.

Section 4 may be invoked on the same grounds as Section 2 (see below) but where it is an urgent necessity that the patient be detained, and undertaking an assessment under Section 2 would cause undesirable delay. Application can be made by an approved social worker or nearest relative, and is founded on the signed medical recommendation of one doctor, if practicable, who knows the patient, for example his GP. The applicant and doctor must have personally seen the patient within the period of 24 hours prior to the application. Section 4 lasts for 72 hours, but within that time can be converted into sections either for admission for assessment (Section 2), or treatment (Section 3).

The use of Section 4 by social workers may well be quite rare: unless clients are homeless, or not known, or the situation is an out-of-town one, their GP and an approved doctor will probably be accessible. Where they are, it is always preferable to use Sections 2 or 3, since they allow for more appropriate means of assessment and, if necessary, treatment for the patient in distress.

ASSESSMENT (SECTION 2)

If, in the above example, a second medical opinion was available, or if the client was not threatening to leave immediately and could be contained until his GP could be found, then Section 2 would be the more appropriate section of the Act to consider.

Section 2 may be invoked where the patient is suffering from:

> 'a mental disorder of a nature or degree which warrants his detention in hospital for assessment (or for assessment followed by medical treatment) *and* he ought to be so detained in the interests of his own health or safety or with a view to the protection of others.'

Application may be made by an approved social worker or the nearest relative, founded on two medical recommendations, one of which must be made by a doctor approved by the Secretary of State for Social Services 'as having special experience in the diagnosis or treatment of mental disorder'. The other medical recommendation should preferably be made by a doctor who knows the patient. If making their examinations separately, no more than five days should elapse between each examination.

Where the approved social worker makes the application, he should take all practicable steps to inform the nearest relative of the application, and of his right to order the patient's discharge. There is no obligation to obtain the nearest relative's agreement prior to making the application.

Application for hospital admission must be made within 14 days of the second medical examination. The patient may be detained for up to 28 days from the time of application.

TREATMENT (SECTION 3)

An example of the use of this section may be where a patient has been admitted to hospital on a voluntary basis, but now wishes to leave. The ward team may well feel that the patient is mentally ill and, if discharged, will put his own health and safety, or that of others, at risk. The patient is well known to the ward team and therefore neither an emergency order nor an assessment order is appropriate. It is felt by the ward team that the patient needs medical treatment which can only be administered in a contained setting.

Criteria

Section 3 of the Mental Health Act can be invoked when it is necessary to detain someone in hospital under medical supervision, which can include 'rehabilitation, habilitation and medical treatment'. (DHSS, 1983). It can be used where informal admission is not appropriate or in respect of someone already in hospital informally, under Sections 2 or 4, or subject to guardianship.

An application for admission for treatment under Section 3(2) may be made on the following grounds:

1. The person is suffering from mental illness, severe mental impairment, psychopathic disorder or mental impairment and his mental disorder is of a nature or degree which makes it appropriate for him to receive medical treatment in hospital; and
2. In the case of psychopathic disorder or mental impairment, such treatment is likely to alleviate or prevent a deterioration of his condition; and
3. It is necessary for the health or safety of the patient or for the protection of other persons that he should receive such treatment and it cannot be provided unless he is detained under this Section.

ADMISSION FOR TREATMENT (SECTION 3)

Treatability requirement

Admission under Section 3 in respect of someone with psychopathic disorder or mental impairment can only be made if the medical recommendations confirm that 'such treatment is likely to alleviate or prevent a deterioration of his condition' and is necessary for the health or safety of the patient or for the protection of other persons.

Treatment need not be expected to cure the patient's disorder and a patient can be admitted under Section 3 if, in the opinion of the doctors making the medical recommendations, medical treatment is likely to enable the patient to cope more satisfactorily with his disorder or its symptoms, or if it stops his condition from becoming worse (DHSS, 1983).

A patient may need to be admitted to hospital for treatment, for instance over a crisis when medication or care is needed, during a stressful life event or period of marked deterioration, even if treatment is unlikely to improve the actual mental impairment or mental illness. However, any renewal of the treatment order can only be made on certain criteria.

Medical recommendations

Two medical recommendations are needed and the general provisions as to medical recommendations apply, as follows.

Only one of the medical recommendations may come from a practitioner on the staff of the hospital to which the patient is to be admitted or detained, except under very exceptional circumstances (see Section 12(4)). Where possible, the other medical recommendation should be from a doctor with previous knowledge of the patient.

In the case of private patients the medical recommendations may not be from doctors on the staff of the hospital.

Both of the medical recommendations must include a clinical description of the patient's mental condition and each recommendation must describe the patient as having one of the same form of disorder, although any of the recommendations may list more than one disorder.

The medical recommendations for admission under Section 3 have also to contain a statement as to whether alternatives to admission are available and, if so, why they are not used.

The medical recommendations must also state the reasons why informal admission is not appropriate.

The medical recommendations have to be completed before an application for admission is made and the doctors making the recommendations must have personally examined the patient, together or separately, and not more than five days elapsed between the separate examinations.

A GP employed part-time in a hospital is *not* regarded as being on that hospital's staff (Section 12(6)), for the purpose of supplying a medical recommendation.

Where one recommendation is made by a consultant the other may not be made by a doctor who works under him (DHSS Memorandum, Para 26 (1983)).

Application

An application for admission under Section 3 can be made by:

1. An approved social worker. This can be an approved social worker acting outside the area by which he is appointed.
2. The nearest relative. The applicant must have seen the patient within 14 days ending with the date of the application and the application has to be supported by 2 medical recommendations.

Social report

When the application for admission for treatment is made by the nearest relative, the hospital managers must inform the local social services authority for the area the patient resided in immediately before his admission. The social services authority must, as soon as practicable, arrange for a social worker to interview the patient and provide the managers with a report on his social circumstances (Section 14).

The social worker making the social circumstances report does not have to be an approved social worker and could be a hospital social worker or area-based social worker. The report should include the patient's social history, family, accommodation, employment and finances and include the suitability and availability of community resources. There could be some dispute as to which social services authority should make the social circumstances report, particularly in respect of a patient of no fixed abode or admitted from temporary accommodation, such as a homeless persons' hostel or squat. The Act refers to the 'area in which the patient resided immediately before his admission'. A patient's last 'residence' could be his marital home or parent's address, provided that he had an intention to return there.

Relatives' right to be consulted

An approved social worker who makes an application under Section 3 of the Mental Health Act is required to take all reasonably practicable steps to consult the nearest relative, if there is one, either before, or within a reasonable time after the application, and advise the relative of the application and his right to object. Contact with the relative could either be personally by the approved social worker, by telephone or letter, or by someone acting on behalf of the approved social worker, i.e. a social worker in another district covering the relative's address. The nearest relative does not have to consent to the admission but he must, if practicable, be informed and be made aware of his right to object. The application for admission under Section 3 cannot be made if the nearest relative signifies his objection (Section 11(4)).

Documents

The applicant is responsible for the delivery of the admission documents to the managers of the hospital and the application form, which should be delivered by hand, must arrive before or at the time of the admission.

The application form requires the following:

1. The applicant to state why, if neither of the medical practitioners knew the patient before the medical recommendations were made, it was not possible to get a recommendation from a medical practitioner who did know the patient prior to the date of the application.

2. If the application is made by an approved social worker he has to state either:

   (a) That he has consulted the nearest relative, who had not notified any objection to the application, or

   (b) It is not reasonably practicable to consult the nearest relative or the nearest relative is not known and there appears to be no relative.

   (c) And that he has interviewed the patient and is satisfied that detention in a hospital is in all the circumstances of the case the most appropriate way of providing the care and medical treatment the patient needs.

The patient must be admitted to hospital within 14 days of the time when he was last medically examined prior to the medical recommendations.

Duration

An admission under Section 3 is, in the first instance, for a period of up to six months from the day of admission. It can be renewed for a period of six months, then yearly.

Renewal

The responsible medical officer has a duty within two months of the end of the detention period to examine the patient and, if he is satisfied that the patient should remain in hospital, he must complete a Renewal of the Authority for Detention (Form 30) addressed to the hospital managers.

Before making a report for Renewal of the Authority for Detention the responsible medical officer must consult one or more other persons who have been professionally concerned with the patient's treatment. The Act does not specify that these have to be professionals from other disciplines and the decision as to whom to consult is that of the responsible medical officer (Section 20(5)).

In order to renew a treatment order under Section 3 the following must apply:

1. The patient is suffering from mental illness, severe mental impairment, psychopathic disorder or mental impairment and his mental disorder is of a nature or degree which makes it appropriate for him to receive medical treatment in a hospital, and
2. That such treatment is likely to alleviate or prevent a deterioration of his condition, and
3. It is necessary for the health or safety of the patient or for the protection of others that he should receive treatment and that it cannot be provided unless he continues to be detained.

In the case of mental illness or severe mental impairment a treatment order under Section 3 may be renewed if, in the opinion of the responsible medical officer, the patient would be unlikely to care for himself, to obtain the care that he needs or to guard against serious exploitation (Section 20(4)). This section will prevent patients who are unlikely to be able to care for themselves from being discharged from hospital unless there are suitable alternatives. A patient cannot be detained under Section 3 if he is willing and able to remain in the hospital as an informal patient. The hospital managers must inform the nearest relative, if there is one, and the patient, that the order has been renewed.

Medical treatment

A patient admitted to hospital under Section 3 can be given certain types of medical treatment without his consent. This is governed by the Code of Practice issued by the Secretary of State and covered by Sections 56 and 64. He can be given a course of medication or drug treatment without his consent for a period of up to three months, after which the psychiatrist in charge of his treatment has to make an evaluation of the treatment and to consider the long-term treatment programme. In the case of emergency a patient can, like any non-psychiatric patient, be given treatment for a medical condition without his consent if such treatment is essential.

Mental health review tribunals (Part V)

The patient has a right to apply to a mental health review tribunal at any time within the first six months of his detention in hospital. If he withdraws his application he can apply again. If the order is renewed, the patient can apply once again in the second six months and once in every subsequent 12 months (Section 66). If the patient does not himself apply to the tribunal after six months, the hospital managers must apply to the tribunal on his behalf.

Discharge

A treatment order under Section 3 is discharged in the following circumstances:

1. At the natural expiration of the period of the order if not renewed, i.e. at the end of the first six months; at the end of the second six months; at the end of each subsequent year.
2. By order of the nearest relative. The nearest relative must give 72 hours notice in writing, or by Form 34, addressed to the hospital managers of his intention to discharge the patient (Section 25(1)). The nearest relative can arrange for a doctor to see the patient and examine him in private for the purpose of advising the relative as to discharge. The responsible medical officer if he considers that, in his opinion, the patient if discharged would be likely to act in a manner dangerous to himself or others, can issue a report barring discharge by the nearest relative (Form 36). The nearest relative must be informed and cannot order discharge for a further six months although he has the right to apply to the review tribunal to consider discharge.
3. By order of the responsible medical officer or by the hospital managers.
4. By order of the Secretary of State if the patient is detained in a mental nursing home or, if the patient is maintained under contract with a health authority, by that authority.
5. By decision of the mental health review tribunal. The patient has the right to apply to the tribunal at any time within the first six months, once during the next six months and yearly thereafter. He can be legally represented. He can ask the tribunal to consider his case by writing to them or to the hospital managers.
6. If reclassified by the responsible medical officer. If the patient is reclassified as suffering from a form of mental disorder other than that specified in the application the authority to detain the patient would cease. Should the responsible medical officer reclassify the patient as suffering from a major to a minor disorder he must state whether the treatability requirement is fulfilled. If it is not, the authority for detention will cease.
7. If he is absent from the hospital without authority or trace for 28 days.

8. After a continual period of six months leave of absence from the hospital.

Leave of absence from the hospital (Section 17)

The responsible medical officer can allow the patient to leave the hospital subject to whatever conditions he thinks necessary in the interests of the patient or other persons. He may grant an indefinite period of leave or specify the exact duration of the leave.

A planned period of leave from the hospital could be a very valuable means of rehabilitating a patient under consideration for discharge. The responsible medical officer can recall a patient at any time by giving notice in writing to the patient or person caring for him. He can also offer support to the person caring during the trial period.

A patient on continuous leave for a period of six months is no longer liable to be detained in hospital.

Missing person

If a patient leaves the hospital without consent he may be taken back into the hospital by a police constable, social worker or anyone authorised by hospital managers. The police should be notified of any missing patient. It is an offence for anyone knowingly to harbour a person liable to be detained under Section 3 or to hinder or obstruct any authorised person trying to find him (Section 128).

If a patient is absent from the hospital without trace for 28 days the order will lapse.

Members of Parliament

The Speaker of the House of Commons must be notified of the admission under Section 3 of a Member of Parliament. The Member will lose his seat in the House if, after being examined immediately after his hospital admission and six months afterwards, he is considered by two specially appointed medical practitioners to be mentally ill and in need of detention (Section 141).

After-care

The local social services authority and health authority have a duty to provide after-care services for patients leaving hospital. This they can do in cooperation with relevant voluntary agencies; and after-care should be provided until such time as the patient is no longer in need of it. The local social services authority is the authority for the area in which the patient is resident or to which he is sent on discharge by the hospital (Section 117).

Other compulsory powers

Of particular relevance to social workers are three other provisions contained in the Mental Health Act 1983 concerning statutory powers. These are:

1. Section 115, concerned with approved social workers' right of entry.
2. Section 135, which is a warrant to send for and remove patients.
3. Section 136, which relates to mentally disordered persons found in public places.

We shall now examine these powers in more detail.

Section 115

Section 115 empowers an approved social worker of a local social services authority to enter and inspect any premises (not a hospital) in the area of that authority in which a mentally disordered person is living, if the social worker has reasonable cause to believe that the patient is not under proper care. This power applies 'at all reasonable times', which will depend upon the urgency of the situation. It is not a power to use force to enter. If entry is refused, caution may be given that such refusal constitutes an offence under Section 129 of the Act. (Section 129 states that any person who forbids an inspection of premises, or an assessment under the Act, or other obstruction without reasonable cause, commits an offence.) If, after the due caution, entry is still refused, the approved social worker may apply for a warrant of entry, under Section 135.

Section 135

An approved social worker may obtain, from a Justice of the Peace, a warrant enabling a constable to enter premises, search for and remove a patient if there is 'reasonable cause to suspect that a person believed to be suffering from mental disorder' has been ill treated, neglected, has not been kept under proper control, or is unable to care for himself and living alone. The warrant must name the constable who is to enter the premises, and the constable must be accompanied by an approved social worker, and a registered medical practitioner.

Section 136

A police officer may remove to a place of safety a person who appears to be 'suffering from mental disorder' and is in 'immediate need of care and control' and who is in a place to which the public have access (for example, a theatre or public highway, etc.). The person can be detained for 72 hours, so that he can be examined and assessed by a doctor and approved social worker. The place of safety can be a police station or a hospital. It is important to note that the purpose of detention is not to provide *custody*, but to enable an *assessment* to be made. Once the assessment has been made, the authority for detention expires, even if 72 hours have not elapsed.

Hospital detention by medical and nursing staff (Section 5)

An application for hospital admission under Sections 2 and 3 may be made in respect of patients who are already in hospital as informal patients. As the patient is already in hospital, this effectively authorises his compulsory detention there.

An informal patient may also be detained for up to 72 hours under Section 5 if the doctor in charge of his treatment reports that an application for admission under Section 2 or 3 ought to be made, and time is needed to obtain the second medical recommendation and assessment by an approved social worker.

Most patients who are admitted for psychiatric treatment on a voluntary basis retain this status throughout their stay. However, there are some patients who, because of a deterioration in their mental state, are unable to sustain a clear judgement about their need for treatment. Such patients often lose sight of the seriousness of their disturbance and the implications this may have for themselves and others. In such cases it is the clear responsibility of the medical practitioner in charge of the case or his nominated deputy or the prescribed nurse to act promptly to prevent such a patient from leaving hospital.

The two main procedures laid down under Section 5 to cope with such situations will now be described.

Section 5(2)

Under this Section an informal patient in a psychiatric hospital or a general hospital may be detained for up to 72 hours if the doctor in charge of his treatment reports that an application for 'admission' ought to be made. The 72 hours takes effect from the time the report is received by the hospital managers.

A second medical recommendation must be obtained during this time period, so that an approved social worker can proceed with assessment and, if appropriate, application for Section 2 or 3.

If the patient leaves hospital he may be retaken within 72 hours of the doctor's report.

Section 5(4)

Under this part of the Section a first level nurse (a registered mental nurse) may detain an informal patient who is already being treated for mental disorder for a period not more than six hours, if it appears to him that:

1. The patient is suffering from mental disorder to such a degree that it is necessary for his health and safety, or for the protection of others, for him to be immediately restrained from leaving the hospital.
2. It is not practicable to secure the immediate attendance of a medical practitioner for the purpose of furnishing a report under Section 5(2).

The 'holding power' starts after the nurse has recorded his opinion on the prescribed form (Form 13) and this ends six hours later, or on the earlier arrival of one of the two doctors (i.e. the responsible medical officer in charge of the case or nominated deputy) entitled to make a report under Section 5(2).

The doctor is free to make such a report or to decide not to detain the patient further (which may, for example, include persuading him to stay voluntarily). The six hour holding period counts as part of the 72 hours, if the doctor concerned decides to make a report under Section 5(2). If the patient leaves hospital he may be retaken within six hours of the nurse's recorded opinion.

Chapter 17
Guardianship

An example of the use of guardianship (Section 7) could be where a person is suffering from a long-standing mental disorder, but who can be maintained in the community; possibly with the assistance of a social worker, community psychiatric nurse, day centre, and other resources. The person may be leading a disorganised and erratic life, occasionally putting himself at great risk by not eating, not taking medication, and living rough. By invoking guardianship powers, a social worker may be able to give this client some structure to his life, make him feel contained, and enable him to gain access to consistent resources and medical treatment, which are his right.

Guardianship is an innovative and important provision made by the 1983 Act, since it allows for fairly intensive therapeutic care to be administered within the community, without recourse to hospitalisation and under social work direction.

WHEN TO USE

Guardianship under Section 7 can provide a means of ensuring care in the community for a mentally disordered person over 16 years of age (or believed to be 16 or over), giving the guardian some specific controls on the lifestyle of the person within his own home, day centre and residential establishment.

In the case of a mentally disordered child under the age of 16, care can be provided under child care legislation, rather than the Mental Health Act, or by informal hospital admission. Section 2 of the Child Care Act 1980, or Section 1 of the Children and Young Persons Act 1969 would be appropriate. Guardianship can provide a 'least restrictive alternative' to hospital admission and should always be considered by the approved social worker, nearest relative and medical practitioners faced with a situation where hospital admission under Section 2 or Section 4 of the Mental Health Act is being considered.

The approved social worker has been given a clear duty to 'satisfy himself that detention in a hospital is in all the circumstances of the case the most appropriate way of providing the care and medical treatment of which the patient stands in need' (Section 13(2)). Therefore, guardianship must be considered and the approved social worker should record on the case file the reasons for it not being appropriate.

PURPOSE

The purpose of guardianship is to provide a realistic alternative to hospital admission and is primarily to ensure that the person receives *care and protection* in the community. It does not enable medical treatment to be given without consent.

CRITERIA

1. The person must be suffering from mental disorder, being mental illness, severe mental impairment, psychopathic disorder or mental impairment as defined in Part I of the Mental Health Act. His mental disorder must be considered by two medical practitioners to be of a nature or degree which warrants his reception into guardianship, and
2. It is necessary in the interests of his *welfare* or for the protection of other people.

POWERS OF THE GUARDIAN (SECTION 8)

The guardian has three essential powers to enable the person under guardianship to be cared for in the community:

1. He can require the person to live in a specified place such as a hostel, group home or in any other accommodation either alone or with specified individuals, including his own family. This residential requirement can be used so that a mentally disordered person does not sleep rough or in inadequate accommodation and can also be used to prevent him from living with people who may exploit or mistreat him.
2. The guardian can require the person to attend specified places at specific times. This could be for medical examination, social work interviews, employment, education, training or social activities.
3. The guardian can require access to the person at the place where he is living to any doctor, approved social worker or any other person

specified by the guardian. This could mean access to a community psychiatric nurse, social worker, home help, relative or voluntary worker, and is a good way to ensure that the person under guardianship is not neglecting himself.

WHO CAN BE APPOINTED AS GUARDIAN?

1. Local social services authority (a designated officer appointed by the authority for the purose).
2. The applicant, who can be an approved social worker or nearest relative.
3. Any other person approved by the local social services authority.

The guardian should be a person who can appreciate the special disabilities and needs of a mentally disordered person and someone who will look after the person in an appropriate way.

The guardian should be interested in promoting the person's physical and mental health and the local social services department must satisfy itself that the proposed guardian is capable of carrying out this function and must assist the guardian with advice and other facilities, such as access to resources. The applicant can name any person, including himself or the local social services authority, as guardian. However, if the guardian named is someone other than the local social services authority, the proposed guardian must first be accepted by the authority for the area in which he lives. The guardian must state in writing that he is willing to act as guardian.

WHO CAN APPLY FOR GUARDIANSHIP?

1. An approved social worker. This can be an approved social worker acting outside the area by which he is appointed.
2. The nearest relative.

The applicant must have seen the person within 14 days ending on the date of the signing of the application for guardianship and the application form must be supported by two medical recommendations.

MEDICAL RECOMMENDATIONS

Two medical recommendations are required and the general provisions as to medical recommendations apply. One of the doctors should be approved for the purpose and, where practicable, one should have had previous acquaintance with the person. If the doctors examine the person separately then not more than five days must elapse between the days on which the separate medical recommendations are completed.

RELATIVES' RIGHT TO OBJECT AND TO BE CONSULTED

The approved social worker must take all reasonably practicable steps to consult the nearest relative, if there is one, either before or within a reasonable time after an application for guardianship is made. The application cannot be made if the nearest relative objects (Section 11(4)).

However, an approved social worker, or anyone else, who considers that the objection of the nearest relative is not in the best interests of the person concerned can apply to the County Court for the appointment of an acting nearest relative to replace any other relative. Such an application to the County Court can only be made on the grounds that the nearest relative is incapable of acting as such by reason of mental disorder or other illness, or is unreasonably objecting to the application for guardianship without proper regard to the welfare of the patient or to the interests of the public (Section 29(3)).

The application form and the medical recommendation(s) have to be forwarded by the applicant to the local social services authority if named as the proposed guardian or to the local social services authority in whose area the proposed guardian lives. This must be done within 14 days of the date of latest medical recommendation.

MEDICAL AND HOSPITAL TREATMENT

A person under guardianship is not compelled to take medical treatment, except in urgent necessity. He can be compelled to be examined by a doctor and required to attend a hospital or health centre for this purpose. If there is a deterioration in his mental state and his doctor considers that he needs to go into hospital he can be admitted as a voluntary patient. Applications for hospital admission may be made under Sections 2 or 4 of the Mental Health Act in the usual way for assessment. Admission under Section 2 or 4 would not affect the guardianship unless the patient were to stay in hospital for more than six months, in which case the guardianship would lapse. Application may also be made for admission to hospital for treatment (Section 3). In this case, the guardianship would lapse (Section 6(4)).

PRISON SENTENCE

If a person who is subject to guardianship is sent to prison for a period exceeding six months the guardianship would lapse.

DURATION

1. Up to six months.
2. Renewal for a further period of six months.
3. Renewal for subsequent periods of one year.

In order to renew, the original grounds for guardianship must remain. The responsible medical officer has to apply for renewal of the guardianship if it appears to him to be necessary in the interests of the person's welfare or the protection of others. He must examine the person during the two months before the guardianship is due to expire and complete a Renewal of Authority of Guardianship (Form 31) and send it to the local social services authority and to the guardian if someone else. The local social services authority must inform the person under guardianship and the nearest relative of the renewal of the Order.

USE BY COURTS

The Crown Court or Magistrate's Court has powers to place an offender under guardianship under the Mental Health Act as an alternative to prison if the Court feels that in all the circumstances, including the nature of the offence, it is the most suitable method of disposing of the case. The offender must be aged 16 or over and suffering from a mental disorder of a nature or degree which would warrant his reception into guardianship. The guardian must be willing to accept guardianship (Section 37(6)).

MISSING PERSON

If the person leaves his accommodation without consent of the guardian he may be taken into custody, and returned to it, by any approved officer of the social services department, police officer, or any other person authorised by the guardian or local social services authority (Section 18(3)).

The police should be notified of any missing person. It is an offence for anyone knowingly to harbour a person under guardianship or to hinder or obstruct any authorised person trying to find him (Section 128).

If a person is absent without trace for 28 days the guardianship will lapse (Section 18(4)).

RIGHT TO ENTER PREMISES

The guardian, or someone appointed by him, has a right to access to the person in his own home. However, he does not have the right to knock down the door or force entry and, should this be necessary, a Magistrate's Order (Section 135) would be required.

REVIEW TRIBUNALS

The person has a right to apply to a mental health review tribunal at any time within the first six months, and once again in the second six months. Subsequently he can only apply once in every 12 months. Guardianship can only be revoked by the tribunal if the original conditions no longer apply.

NOMINATED DOCTOR

A person under guardianship must have a nominated doctor. This will usually be his GP, if he has one, who has had the care of his general health and will continue to be responsible and to be involved in recommendations as to the continuation of the guardianship order. It is the responsibility of the guardian to arrange for the appointment of a nominated doctor. Where the guardian is a local social services authority they must appoint a 'responsible medical practitioner', usually a consultant psychiatrist, who has the power to discharge the patient from guardianship.

DISCHARGE

A guardianship order is discharged in the following circumstances:

1. At the natural expiration of the period of the order if not renewed, i.e. at the end of the first six months; at the end of the second six months; at the end of each subsequent year.
2. By order of the nearest relative. The nearest relative cannot be barred from making an order for discharge and it becomes effective as soon as the relative delivers a Notice of Discharge (Form 35) to the local social services authority. The relative has the right to arrange for any doctor to see the person and examine him in private for the purpose of advising the relative as to discharge.
3. By order of the responsible medical officer or local social services authority. The decision to make the order should be made by three or more members of the local social services authority, or by a sub-committee of the health authority. A Form of Discharge (Form 36) must be sent to the nearest relative.

4. By decision of a mental health review tribunal. The person has the right to apply to the review tribunal for the discharge of the guardianship order at any time during the first six months. Afterwards, he can apply once during the next six months and yearly thereafter. He can be legally represented. He can ask the tribunal to look at his case by writing to them.
5. If the person is admitted to hospital for treatment under Section 3 under the Mental Health Act.
6. If he is absent without trace for 28 days.

RENEWAL OF GUARDIANSHIP

A person under guardianship must be examined by the responsible medical officer or the nominated medical attendant during the two months before the authority for guardianship is due to expire. The guardianship can only be renewed if the original conditions relating to the making of the order continue to apply and it appears to the doctor that it is necessary in the interests of the welfare of the patient or for the protection of other persons.

The responsible medical officer has to complete a Renewal of Authority for Detention (Form 30) and the local social services authority is responsible for informing the person, and the nearest relative, and advising them of their rights to apply again to the tribunal or for the relative to order discharge.

TRANSFER OF GUARDIANSHIP (SECTION 19)

A person subject to guardianship may, with the consent of the guardian, move into another area. If guardianship is still required the guardianship can be transferred to another social services authority and no new application would be needed.

CHANGE OF RESIDENCE

A person subject to guardianship cannot move address without the consent of the guardian who has to be satisfied that the new home is suitable and in his best interests. A social services authority, acting as guardian, can arrange for the person to live outside its own area, perhaps in a group home, voluntary organisation or with some approved individual able to offer care. This may be on a permanent or a temporary basis but, so long as the social services authority remains guardian, it continues to be responsible for the welfare and supervision of the person but can arrange for another authority or organisation to visit and make reports.

GUARDIAN NOT WISHING, OR BEING UNABLE, TO CONTINUE

A guardian who does not wish to continue the guardianship can give notice in writing to the social services authority that he wishes to give up the guardianship. On receipt of the notice the guardianship is transferred to the local social services authority.

Guardianship is automatically transferred to the local social services on the death of the guardian. If the guardian is ill or unable for any other cause to perform the functions of guardian, those duties may be performed during the incapacity by the local social services, or someone acting on their behalf. But they are nevertheless acting as agent for the guardian and may not go against any expressed wishes of the guardian (Section 10(2)).

UNSATISFACTORY GUARDIANS

If the guardian is considered, by the responsible social services authority, to be neglecting the person for whom they are guardian, or if they are not acting in his best interests, then an approved social worker can apply to the County Court for guardianship to be transferred to the social services authority, or to some other person approved for the purpose by that authority (Section 10(3)).

Chapter 18
Rights of Patients and Relatives

RIGHTS OF PATIENTS

The spirit of the Mental Health Act 1983 is oriented towards ensuring that the rights of the mentally ill are respected, from the duty laid upon approved social workers to seek care for the compulsory patient in the 'least restrictive setting', to the ready access once inside hospital to mental health review tribunals. The requirements of assessment under Sections 2, 3 and 4 are themselves designed to protect the interest of patients, and therefore it is important for approved social workers to take account of these when making an application for admission. These are set out elsewhere in this book. There are other factors however which are not so clearly set out and it may be helpful to clarify them here.

RIGHT OF INTERVIEW IN A SUITABLE MANNER

Approved social workers are given the responsibility of interviewing the patient being assessed for admission in a suitable manner and satisfy themselves that detention in hospital is in all the circumstances of the case the most appropriate way of providing the care and medical treatment of which the patient stands in need (Section 13(2)).

INFORMATION

Patients have the right to receive information concerning their compulsory detention—and it is the duty of the approved social worker and hospital to explain their rights to them. The hospital must do this in writing (Section 132).

MENTAL HEALTH REVIEW TRIBUNALS

The Act makes provision for ready appeal to tribunals, and where no appeal is made by the patient, for automatic appeal after a period of time.

1. Where a patient is admitted for assessment (Section 2), he can apply within the first 14 days of admission.
2. Where a patient is admitted for treatment (Section 3), the patient can apply within the first six months of admission and during each period of renewal.
3. Where the patient is received into guardianship (Section 7) he can apply within the first six months, during the next six months, and during each subsequent period of one year.

Where a patient detained under Section 3 has not been reviewed by the tribunal within the first six months there is automatic review by the tribunal. Subsequently, an automatic review is held every three years unless the patient appeals in the interim. Legal Aid is available for patients who wish to be represented by a solicitor, but who do not have financial means to pay for their own legal representation.

In addition to the mental health review tribunal, the Act established the Mental Health Act Commission. This can receive complaints made by detained patients concerning either the Mental Health Act and its operation, or other matters such as alleged maltreatment and misappropriation of personal property. Complaints must first be made to the hospital managers. The commission will investigate if they consider that the managers did not deal with the complaint in a satisfactory way.

IN-PATIENT RIGHTS

The principle upheld by the Act is that compulsorily detained patients—and informal mentally ill patients—should enjoy the same rights as other patients in general hospitals.

Informal patients

Informal patients retain most of their rights of citizenship. Their correspondence cannot be withheld; they have the right to vote, subject to their ability to declare without assistance (unless blind or physically disabled) that they are an informal mental patient. They must give the address in the UK where they would be resident if they were not a mental patient. If they cannot give such an address, any UK address—other than a mental hospital—at which they have resided, is acceptable. The hospital managers must give informal patients notice that they are entitled to do this.

Informal patients retain the right of access to the courts. The right to receive visitors, keep clothing, make complaints, etc. should be the same as those for patients in a general hospital.

Compulsorily detained patients

There are provisions under the Act which limit the rights of compulsorily detained patients. Although where possible, the spirit of the Act is to maintain as little a distinction as is practicable between compulsorily detained patients and any other patient being treated in a general hospital for a physical illness.

Post sent by a detained patient can be withheld if the addressee has so requested. Post sent to a detained patient may not be read or withheld (Section 134). Detained patients cannot be entered on the electoral register in any circumstances.

Access to the courts for detained patients is limited. This is especially the case where a patient wishes to sue someone in connection with their admission under the Mental Health Act (Section 139). The patient needs permission to initiate civil proceedings from the High Court, and from the Director of Public Prosecutions in order to initiate criminal proceedings. In order to be able to sue in connection with a compulsory admission, the patient must be able to show reasonable grounds to indicate that the person he seeks to sue acted in bad faith or without reasonable care. It does not matter whether that person had jurisdiction to act. He has the full protection of the law provided he carried out what he believed were his legitimate duties under the Act in good faith and with reasonable care.

THE MANAGEMENT OF PATIENT'S PROPERTY AND AFFAIRS: THE COURT OF PROTECTION

The responsibilities of the Court of Protection are set out in Part VII of the Mental Health Act 1983. The Court of Protection is the official body which can take over and manage the property and affairs of a mentally ill person. This person need not be in hospital—he can reside in the community. Irrespective of this, the Court terms him a patient. Once a person is deemed mentally incapable of managing his affairs, he cannot then give power of attorney to anyone else to manage his property.

The criterion for a person to come under the Court's jurisdiction are that he 'is incapable, by reason of mental disorder, of managing and administering his property and affairs'. The procedure is to obtain one medical recommendation. This need not necessarily be from a doctor with special experience of mental illness, it can be the patient's GP.

An order under the Court of Protection lasts indefinitely, until it is revoked. The effect of an order is that the Court can manage and control a patient's property and affairs. It also has the power to appoint a receiver, who can be a relative, the Director of the local social services authority, or the Official Solicitor.

Case illustration

An example of the use of the Court of Protection can be seen in the case of a woman aged 40 with a long history of mental illness. She had a diagnosis of chronic schizophrenia, but with medication and community support such as social worker and community psychiatric nurse, could live and would rather have lived in her own flat. However, because of the confusion and delusions engendered by her illness, the patient could not keep track of her finances. She would often rip giros up as they came through the door. When she had an Order Book she drew from it erratically and often gave large sums away in the street. Bills went unpaid, including her rent. The patient was put under a Court of Protection with the local authority Director of Social Services as appointee. All DHSS giros and bills were then immediately picked up and dealt with by the appointee (who in this case was the local authority's Finance Officer). He ensured a regular weekly amount was made over to the patient—who could always approach him for an increase or decrease in this amount. The patient was able to continue living in her flat in the normal way, without the additional stresses of having to manage and budget her own money.

Patients who are unhappy with any decision made by the court can appeal to the High Court. Any hardship caused by maladministration can be investigated by the Parliamentary Commissioner for Administration.

The address of the Court of Protection is: 25 Store Street, London WC1.

RIGHTS IN THE COMMUNITY

In addition to patients' rights in hospital, it is important also to note that the mentally ill have special rights within the community. The particular importance for social workers is that the Mental Health Act 1983, confers the duty upon social services authorities, in cooperation with voluntary agencies, to provide prevention, care, and after-care services for those patients who have been detained for treatment under Section 3. According to the 1983 Act (Section 117) this duty to provide after-care is required to stay in force until the patient no longer has need of such services.

The other major arm in statutory community care of the mentally ill is, of course, the Housing (Homeless Persons) Act 1977. Section 1 of this Act states that a person is homeless if he has no accommodation which he is entitled to occupy; Section 2 states that a person has priority need for accommodation if he is 'vulnerable as a result of mental illness, or handicap or other special reason'; while Section 4 imposes the duty upon housing departments to provide accommodation for people who are homeless, or threatened with homelessness if they have a priority need.

These rights can be enforced by, or on behalf of, the mentally ill. However, it must also be remembered in negotiations with housing departments that it is the local authority with whom the applicant has a local connection which is under statutory obligation to provide accommodation. Thus if a social worker is presented with a case of homelessness where the client has moved around the country, or has not lived in any one area for any length of time, difficulties can arise. If the client has absolutely no fixed abode then their local connection will generally be either with the area where they are at that moment in time; or, if this is a matter of days (or hours), the area where they have most recently lived the longest.

Most local authority housing departments will, in any case, have their own guidelines, and it is advisable for social workers to become acquainted with these if working with homeless, or potentially homeless, clients. In addition, most urban authorities have, since 1977, set up Homeless Person's Units which specialise in the implementation of the Homeless Person's Act. It can be very helpful for social workers to have good working relationships with officers in these departments so that referrals can be made easily and, often, advice can be obtained over the telephone.

In any event, it can obviously save much time, effort and headaches, if a client's local connection can be established before lengthy negotiations with housing departments are entered into.

WELFARE BENEFITS

On becoming mentally ill, a client's financial affairs often disintegrate. This can be even more the case when they are admitted to a mental hospital. Clients who are working will be eligible for Sickness Benefit. Clients who are not—and they are many—must rely on Supplementary Benefit. The latter is usually referred to as Social Security. In addition, many clients may be on Housing Benefit. All these benefits, complex enough in themselves, become even more so to the mentally ill mind. Social workers can play an important role in helping clients sort out their benefit difficulties, and ensure that muddle, although probably unavoidable, is kept to a minimum.

To assist with this, we have set out below some of the major aspects of Welfare Benefit rights (as of Summer 1985—subject to governmental review) as they pertain to social workers and their mentally ill clients. We do not provide benefit rates as these fluctuate, and are available in leaflet form from DHSS offices. Neither do we try to cover every eventuality. If situations occur which are not discussed below, readers should refer to works listed in the bibliography at the end of Chapter 19, as well as discussing the matter with their local DHSS office.

Supplementary Benefit

This is a means tested benefit available whether or not a client has worked. Single, childless people going into hospital on Supplementary Benefit will have their benefit reduced to a flat rate, weekly sum for the duration of their hospital stay. This amounts to pocket money and is justified on the grounds that food and other day-to-day expenses are met by the hospital. This is called the hospital in-patient allowance.

The DHSS will continue to pay for a claimant's rent if they were already doing so, including a retaining fee for board and lodgings, unless the claimant is likely to be away for more than a year. Where the client is in receipt of Supplementary Benefit but has a mortgage, the DHSS will pay the mortgage interest, but not capital repayments.

Couples

If one of a couple is in hospital, their full normal benefit and any housing requirements will continue for the first eight weeks. Certain weekly additions for special needs will go, as given below. After eight weeks, benefit is reduced slightly. After two years in hospital, or earlier if it is apparent that the patient is there permanently, a married couple is no longer classified as a couple. The couple will be treated as separate individuals for benefit purposes.

If both members of a couple are in hospital, their normal requirements are reduced substantially, unless they have dependent children (in which case benefit goes on in full for eight weeks). After eight weeks, they are reduced to the hospital in-patient allowance each, unless they have children for whom they continue to receive an allowance.

Single parents

For single parents, the position is more complex and for information on this and other matters in connection with children of claimants, readers are referred to the more specialised literature listed in the bibliography at the end of Chapter 19.

Housing Benefit

Claimants continue to be eligible for Housing Benefit while in hospital.

State Sickness Benefit

Claimants who are receiving Sickness Benefit on admission continue to receive their full rate of Sickness Benefit for eight weeks. It is then reduced by about a third. After one year it goes down to correspond with the hospital in-patient allowance, Supplementary Benefit rate.

Other changes for claimants' benefit on going into hospital are as follows.

Immediately: They lose the weekly additions for heating, attendance needs, bathing, diet, domestic assistance, laundry, extra wear on clothing.

Four weeks in hospital: If single, or a single parent whose children are not staying at home, claimant will lose heating additions given because their home is difficult to heat or because they have central heating. If claimants have to pay a separate fixed charge for heating with their rent, they may qualify for a heating addition towards the cost of any increase in the heating additions they normally receive.

Fares

Patients on Supplementary Benefit or Family Income Supplement, or patients with net income on or below the Supplementary Benefit level can claim for fares, either as out-patients, or as in-patients at the start and end of their stay. They need to apply on form H11. This form is available either from the hospital or from the DHSS. Close relatives or members of the household receiving Supplementary Benefit can obtain fares to visit the patient in hospital.

Leaving hospital

On going into/leaving hospital, patients may be eligible to receive certain grants:

1. Clothing. A single payment for clothing may be made if the patient

or the family needs extra items to stay in hospital, e.g. pyjamas. In addition, on discharge a grant may be made for extra clothing if the need has arisen 'otherwise than by wear and tear'. Patients already in hospital are expected to clothe themselves by means of their hospital in-patient allowance.

2. Resettlement. If the patient has been in hospital for over a year, or if he was homeless on admission and housing has been obtained to which he will go, a grant may be made towards furniture and resettlement, etc. Discussions on this may need to be entered into with local DHSS offices well before any planned discharges are made.

Patients' affairs

While in hospital, patients' property and effects are looked after by the hospital's administration division, which may be well acquainted with individual in-patients and their benefit position.

CONSENT TO TREATMENT

The legal position of a detained mental patient concerning consent to, or refusal of, treatment is clarified under Part IV of the Mental Health Act 1983. We set out below the main provisions as they apply to social workers and their clients. For a more wide ranging analysis readers should refer to the reference material listed in the bibliography at the end of Chapter 19.

Exclusions from the Act: common law rights

Part IV of the Act does not apply to informal patients, nor to those detained under short-term orders (Sections 4 and 136 are the most relevant exclusions for social workers), nor to guardianship patients. Patients who are so excluded have the same rights to refuse treatment as does any patient admitted to a general hospital with a physical disorder. This is a right under common law. Where such patients cannot give consent but are not withholding consent (e.g. a demented patient), and the situation is not an emergency, the nearest relative should be approached for consent. If there is no nearest relative, a court order should be considered.

Under common law medical treatment without consent may be given in an emergency or in cases of necessity. Necessity is not defined in law, but it mainly covers instances of unconsciousness, accidents and lifesaving measures. In most cases the responsibility for taking such decisions lies with the doctor.

Where Part IV applies

As we have said, this includes patients compulsorily admitted for 28 days or longer, that is, Sections 2 and 3. The Act sets out three categories of medical treatment: Category 1, psychosurgery and sex hormone implant treatment; Category 2, medication after it has been administered for three months, and ECT; Category 3, any other treatment for mental disorder administered under the direction of the responsible medical officer.

Category 1: psychosurgery and sex hormone implant treatment
The statutory authority for this is Section 57. Under this section, treatment cannot be given unless the patient consents *and a second opinion agrees*: this consent must be confirmed by a doctor other than the responsible medical officer and also two other non-medical persons, all appointed by the Mental Health Act Commission. Before issuing a certificate to proceed with the treatment the doctor must consult two other people who have been concerned with the patient's treatment, one a nurse and the other neither a nurse nor a doctor.

Section 57 also applies to informal patients, in view of the potentially irreversible nature of the treatment.

Category 2: medication after it has been administered for three months and ECT
The statutory authority for this is Section 58. Under this section treatment cannot be given unless the patient agrees, or a second opinion agrees. The responsible medical officer or a doctor appointed by the Mental Health Act Commission must certify in writing that the patient is capable of comprehending what the treatment is, its effects and purpose; and has consented to it. Where consent from the patient is not given, then a doctor appointed by the commission (not the responsible medical officer) must certify in writing that the patient is not capable of comprehending the treatment, or has not consented to it, but that 'having regard to the likelihood of it alleviating or preventing a deterioration of his condition, the treatment should be given'.

Before issuing the certificate to proceed with treatment the independent doctor must consult two other people who have been professionally concerned with the patient's medical treatment—one a nurse, the other neither a nurse nor a doctor.

Withdrawal of consent

Section 60 provides that a patient can withdraw his consent to treatment at any time, except for cases of emergency. This is also a basic right under common law.

Category 3: any other treatment

This can range from nursing to psychoanalysis, and includes most of the day-to-day therapeutic activities within hospital. The patient can be treated without consent or a second opinion.

Urgent treatment

Under Section 62 any treatment to which Part IV of the Act applies can be administered without the need for consent or a second opinion if it is urgent. This means that it is necessary to save the patient's life, is not irreversible, and is immediately necessary to prevent a serious deterioration in the patient's condition, or prevent harm to others.

RIGHTS OF RELATIVES

The Mental Health Act 1983 confers a number of rights onto the nearest relative. Essentially these are: rights to do with admission; rights to do with discharge; rights to receive information; rights of application to mental health review tribunals.

NEAREST RELATIVE

Definitions of relative and nearest relative are contained in Section 26 of the Mental Health Act 1983. The nearest relative may make applications for compulsory detention or for guardianship and where practicable, must be consulted before an application for admission for treatment or guardianship is made by an approved social worker, who may not make the application if the nearest relative objects. The nearest relative is also empowered to discharge the patient in certain circumstances.

Fig. 18.1 gives the hierarchical position of relatives and refers to the following notes.

Note

1. *Elder* of any group has preference, regardless of sex.
2. Relatives of *half blood* are treated as full blood and illegitimate treated as legitimate child of his mother.
3. Relative caring for someone has preference over all other relatives if

he is 'caring' on a daily basis, even if he does not share residence. This means a relative who shops, cooks and does housework for someone unable to do it themselves.

4. Husband or wife includes a person who is living with the patient as patient's husband or wife, whether or not legally married. This applies to husband or wife who has lived with the patient for a period of not less than six months of that period prior to admission to hospital. A person living with married patient is disregarded if the patient is not permanently separated either by agreement or Court Order or by period of desertion.

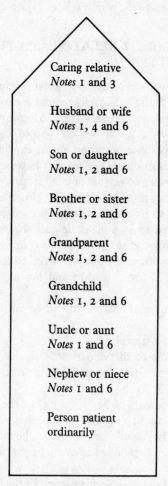

Caring relative
Notes 1 and 3

Husband or wife
Notes 1, 4 and 6

Son or daughter
Notes 1, 2 and 6

Brother or sister
Notes 1, 2 and 6

Grandparent
Notes 1, 2 and 6

Grandchild
Notes 1, 2 and 6

Uncle or aunt
Notes 1 and 6

Nephew or niece
Notes 1 and 6

Person patient
ordinarily

Fig. 18.1 Hierarchy of nearest relative.

5. Someone the patient has resided with (or did so before admission to hospital) for a period of not less than five years. Does not apply to married patient unless husband or wife disregarded. (See (4).)

6. Relatives ascertained as if 'dead' (i.e. not consulted) as follows:

   (a) Relatives not resident in UK, Channel Islands or Isle of Man when patient usually lives in one of these places.

   (b) Husband or wife, permanently separated by agreement, Court Order or desertion.

   (c) Under 18 years except for husband, wife, father and mother.

   (d) Person against whom an order under Section 38 of Sexual Offences Act 1956, which relates to incest, has been made.

WRITING TO NEAREST RELATIVE (SECTION 13(4)): OUTLINE OF LETTER

When the nearest relative of an individual is concerned about that person's mental health, he or she may require the social services department to appoint an approved social worker to look into the case as soon as possible. The approved social worker should consider whether an application for admission is required and is expected to exercise professional judgment. Section 13(4) does not, however, stipulate that the client has to be interviewed or that any other 'professionals', who have knowledge of the case, must be consulted. However, it would be good social work practice to interview or consult everyone concerned.

When the approved social worker decides that an application is not required, he has to inform the nearest relative, in writing, of the reasons for this decision. This responsibility to write to the nearest relative is given to the approved social worker and not to the employing local authority.

The letter to the nearest relative should be on the following lines:

Dear .... [relative's name]

You wrote to/contacted this department on .... [date] expressing your concern, as the nearest relative, about the mental health of .... [client's name].

Under the requirements of Section 13(4) of the Mental Health Act 1983 I was appointed to consider .... [his/her] case and decide whether .... [he/she] should be admitted to hospital. I have discussed the case with you .... [and/or] .... [client's name] general practitioner.

I have interviewed .... [client's name]. In the light of these discussions .... [and/or] this interview, my professional opinion is that

.... [client's name] should not be admitted to and detained in hospital under the Mental Health Act 1983. The reason for this decision is that:

(a) ...... [client's name] mental state does not come within the definitions of mental disorder which may require admission and detention in hospital as laid down by the law. (This opinion is medically confirmed.)

or

(b) Although I believe that an application to hospital under the Mental Health Act 1983 should be made in .... [client's name] interest, ... [one/or two] of the doctors who examined .... [him/ her] would not support my recommendation for such an application.

or

(c) Although .... [client's name] mental disorder does merit an application for admission to hospital, and the two doctors who examined .... [him/her] confirm this opinion, I do not believe that an admission to hospital is in .... [his/her] best interests.

I would recommend that the following course of action is taken: [Approved social worker should then give details of alternative care, i.e. community psychiatric nursing, day hospital, out-patients, day centre, etc.]

or

I consider that .... [client's name] will benefit far more if .... [he/she] remains in .... [his/her] present situation with the existing supports.

I shall be pleased to discuss my decision with you. If you are not satisfied with this opinion you do have the right as the nearest relative to apply for an admission to hospital. Your application must be supported by two medical recommendations which confirm that .... [client's name] mental disorder is such that an admission to hospital for assessment or treatment is necessary. I can advise you on the procedures you have to follow, and can provide you with and assist you in the completion of the forms you need. If you decide on this course of action, and .... [client's name] is admitted, the hospital will ask me to provide a report on .... [his/her] social circumstances which will include my opinion as stated above. My office is open from .... [hours a.m.] to .... [hours p.m.] and my telephone extension is ...... Please do not hesitate to contact me if you would like to discuss the matter further.

Yours faithfully,

approved social worker

ADMISSIONS BY NEAREST RELATIVE

The nearest relative can apply for admission for assessment (Sections 2 and 4); he can apply for an admission for treatment (Section 3); and he can apply for reception into guardianship (Sections 7 and 11(1)). The requirements for an application—including the medical recommendations—are the same, whether an application is made by a nearest relative or approved social worker. This means in effect that it is either the nearest relative or the approved social worker who can make the application for admission under the Act.

It could be commented that where there is an option to apply for admission—between approved social worker and nearest relative—thought needs to be given as to who is the most appropriate applicant. As a general principle it is probably preferable for an approved social worker to make the application. Relatives can be made to feel distress and guilt at the thought that they have 'committed' their loved one to a mental hospital. Family relationships may suffer additional stress which can harm the family's, and the patient's, abilities to come together again after the illness has subsided.

Consultation with relative

The nearest relative can request their local social services authority to consider the compulsory admission of a person to a mental hospital. When such a request is made, social services have a duty to direct an approved social worker as soon as practicable, to decide whether or not a compulsory order needs to be made.

It is not stated in the Act that the social worker must interview the client; although it is hard to see how this can be avoided. The emphasis is on the approved social worker looking at the facts and making a professional judgement. If in this case the approved social worker decides not to make an application he must inform the nearest relative of his decision and his reason, in writing (Section 13(4)).

Under Sections 2 and 4 of the Act, which are admissions for assessment, all practical steps should be taken by the approved social worker to inform the nearest relative of the admission and of his power of discharge—which we will discuss below (Section 11(3)).

Under Sections 3 and 7 of the Act, which are to do with admissions for treatment and reception into guardianship, respectively, the position is more complex. The approved social worker must, if practical, consult with the nearest relative and take account of his wishes and directions. If the nearest relative has notified objections in advance then the admission or reception should not take place. The approved social worker can only proceed under Sections 3 and 7 without consultation with the nearest relative if in his/her opinion such consultation would involve unreasonable delay or is not reasonably practicable (Section 11(4)).

DISCHARGE BY NEAREST RELATIVE

The nearest relative has the power to order the discharge of a patient detained in hospital under Sections 2, 3 and 7; not under Section 4.

Detentions for assessment or treatment (Sections 2 and 3)

The nearest relative must first give 72 hours notice in writing to the managers of the hospital. If, within this time, the doctor in charge of the patient's care—the responsible medical officer—gives a report to the hospital managers stating that in his opinion, the patient, if discharged, 'would be likely to act in a manner dangerous to other persons or himself', then the order for discharge made by the nearest relative will be void (Sections 23(2) and 25(1)). In these circumstances the nearest relative can make no further order for discharge until a period of six months has elapsed (Section 25(1)(b)).

If the responsible medical officer furnishes a report barring the patient's discharge in the case of a person admitted for treatment, the nearest relative can, within the subsequent 28 days, apply to a mental health review tribunal requesting the patient's discharge (Section 66).

The hospital managers have a duty to inform the nearest relative if the doctor furnishes a report to the effect that, in his opinion, the patient would be a danger to himself if discharged (Section 25(2)).

The nearest relative who is considering the discharge of a patient can appoint any registered medical practitioner to visit the patient. Such a doctor may then, at any reasonable time, visit and examine the patient in private. He can have access to the patient's case notes and any other material relating to the detention or treatment of the patient in hospital (Section 24(1) and (2)).

Guardianship (Section 7)

In the case of a patient subject to guardianship there is no requirement for 72 hours notice of discharge to be given by the nearest relative. The nearest relative's discharge order cannot be barred by the responsible medical officer or any other person.

ACCESS TO INFORMATION

The Act confers on to the hospital managers several duties with regard to giving information to the nearest relative. It gives hospital managers the duty, where practicable, to give the nearest relative seven days notice of the intention to discharge the patient. This is the case unless the nearest relative or the patient has requested that the nearest relative not be informed (Section 133). It gives hospital managers the duty to provide relatives with written information which sets out under which section of the Act the patient is being detained, the effect of that section and the rights of application to a mental health review tribunal (Section 132(4)).

Where relevant to the particular case, hospital managers are given the duty to provide written information to the nearest relative concerning the following:

1. Orders for discharge (Section 23).
2. Restrictions on discharge by nearest relative (Section 25).
3. Consent to treatment (Sections 56–64).
4. Application to a mental health review tribunal concerning a medical report contesting a nearest relative's order for discharge (Section 66(1)(g)).
5. The function of the Secretary of State regarding codes of practice and the protection of detained patients (Sections 118 and 120).
6. Censorship of correspondence to and from patients (Sections 134, and 132(2) as applied by 132(4)).

Rights of patient

It is important to note within all these provisions, that if the patient so requests, no information can be supplied by the hospital managers to the nearest relative.

Objections to the nearest relative exercising his rights

Under the Act, provisions are also made for the appointment of someone other than the nearest relative to take on the powers of that relative with regard to the patient. Any relative of the patient, or any person with whom the patient is living, or was living when admitted, or an approved social worker may apply to have himself or any other person appointed as the patient's nearest relative for the purposes of the Act. Such an application is made to the County Court under Section 29 of the Act. It must be made on one of the following grounds:

1. That the patient has no known nearest relative within the meaning of the Act.
2. That the nearest relative is incapable of acting by reason of mental disorder or other illness.
3. That the nearest relative unreasonably objects to the making of an application for admission for treatment or reception into guardianship.
4. That the nearest relative has exercised without due regard to the welfare of the patient, or the interests of the public, his power to discharge the patient from hospital or guardianship.

It is also important to note that such a 'displacement order' may be discharged or varied upon application to the County Court (Section 30) and there are County Court rules setting out the procedures for applications (Section 31). The nearest relative must apply to the County Court within one year after his displacement and subsequently in each period of one year for which the order is in force.

APPLICATION TO MENTAL HEALTH REVIEW TRIBUNAL

The nearest relative can apply in certain circumstances to have the patient's case brought before a mental health review tribunal for review. There are several occasions where this can be done, but the most important for social workers are discussed below. We have not included here occasions under Part III of the Act, where patients are concerned in criminal proceedings or under sentence.

It is also important to note that the Act makes provision for automatic reference to the tribunal according to the definitions under each section. In addition, patients also have extensive rights of appeal. Readers are referred to the relevant chapters elsewhere for a discussion of these aspects of the Act.

Admission for treatment (Section 3)

The nearest relative can apply to the tribunal within 28 days after being informed that the responsible medical officer has issued a report barring the nearest relative from discharging the patient. This means that the relative must first apply to have the patient discharged.

Reclassification

Where the patient has been reclassified as suffering from a different form of mental disorder (Section 16), the nearest relative can apply to the tribunal within 28 days after reclassification.

Chapter 19
Social Reports

Where a patient is admitted to hospital on the application of the nearest relative under Section 2 (assessment) or Section 3 (treatment) of the Mental Health Act 1983, the hospital managers must notify the local social services authority, covering the patient's address immediately before admission, as soon as possible. The social services department must then arrange for a social worker to interview the patient and provide the hospital managers with a social circumstances report (Section 14).

SOCIAL WORKER

It is important to understand the definition of this term. Section 14 clearly states that a 'social worker' should interview the patient. There is no requirement that it be an approved social worker. The social worker who makes the report should be decided as follows:

1. Where the patient is known to a social worker (i.e. an active case) that social worker should prepare the report.
2. Where the patient is not known, but an approved social worker has already assessed the case at the request of the nearest relative under Section 13(4) that approved social worker should prepare the report.
3. In all other instances, where possible the hospital social worker should prepare the report.

SOCIAL CIRCUMSTANCES REPORT

This report is an important document, in that it may determine the status of the patient, e.g. the need for the patient to be compulsorily detained and the duration of the detention. The report should be structured in the following way:

1. Patient's name, full address and date of birth.
2. Name and address of the patient's GP.

3. State whether you are the patient's social worker under (1) in the previous section (with the date the case was allocated to you), under (2) in the previous section (with relevant dates) or under (3) in the previous section.
4. Patient's history. This should include the family background and past mental disorder (in a social rather than medical context).
5. Patient's present circumstances: home environment, family relationships and involvement, social relationships, employment, income, services received in the community, recent changes/ incidents/personal factors that may have affected the patient detrimentally and help to explain the present crisis.
6. Patient's views and wishes. This should include details of the patient's knowledge of the right, and his/her wish, to apply to the mental health review tribunal to achieve his/her own discharge.
7. The views of the nearest relative/other relatives/closely involved persons and their wishes in respect of the patient.
8. If the social circumstances report is being prepared by an approved social worker under (2) in the previous section he/she should include the reasons for his/her decision not to apply for an admission.

To obtain the information for the report the social worker may wish to consult with other professionals involved. It must be remembered that a Section 2 admission detains a patient for a maximum of 28 days, and that the patient has the right to apply to the mental health review tribunal within the first 14 days of his/her detention. The social worker must be prepared to complete the social circumstances report quickly in the interests of the patient and his/her family.

REFERENCES AND FURTHER READING

Legislation and statutory instruments

The Health and Social Services and Social Security Adjudications Act 1983. London: HMSO.
The Housing (Homeless Persons) Act 1977. London: HMSO.
The Mental Health Act 1983. London: HMSO.
The Mental Health Act Commission (Establishment and Constitution) Order 1983. London: HMSO.
The Mental Health Act Commission Regulations 1983. London: HMSO.
The Mental Health (Hospital, Guardianship and Consent to Treatment) Regulations 1983. London: HMSO.
The Mental Health Review Tribunal Rules of Procedure 1983. London: HMSO.
The National Health Service Act 1977. London: HMSO.

Government documents and reports

Committee on Mentally Abnormal Offenders (Lord Butler), Cmnd 6244 (1975). London: HMSO.

Department of Health and Social Security (1983). *Mental Health Act 1983 Explanatory Memorandum*. London: HMSO.

Mental Health Act Commission. *Code of Practice*. London: HMSO (in press).

Reform of Mental Health Legislation, Cmnd 8405 (1981). London: HMSO.

Review of the Mental Health Act 1959 (1976). London: HMSO.

Review of the Mental Health Act 1959, Cmnd 7320 (1978). London: HMSO.

Royal Commission on the Law Relating to Mental Illness and Mental Deficiency (Lord Percy) 1954–1957, Cmnd 189 (1957). London: HMSO.

OTHER REFERENCES

Allbeson J., Douglas J. (1985). *National Welfare Benefits Handbook*. London: Child Poverty Action Group.

Approved Social Workers: MIND's Open Letter to the Secretary of State (1984). *Bull. R. Coll. Psychiatrists*; **December**: 234.

Bean P., ed. (1983). *Mental Illness: Changes and Trends*. Chichester: Wiley.

Bluglass R. (1983). *A Guide to the Mental Health Act*. London: William Heinemann.

Bluglass R. (1984). The origin of the Mental Health Act 1983. *Bull. R. Coll. Psychiatrists*; **July**: 127–33.

Coote A., Gill T. (1982). *Women's Rights*. London: Penguin.

Department of Health and Social Security (1984). *Supplementary Benefits Handbook*. London: HMSO.

Directory of Projects: England and Wales 1982–83 (1982). London: Taylor Hall Publishing, in association with MIND, NACRO and FARE.

Fenton T. W. (1984). The aftermath of the Mental Health Act 1983: some preliminary impressions. *Bull. R. Coll. Psychiatrists*; **October**: 190–3.

Fisher M., Newton C. (1985). Coming up to expectation. *Community Care*, 28 March.

Gostin L. (1975, 1977). *A Human Condition* (two volumes). London: MIND.

Gostin L. (1983). *A Practical Guide to Mental Health Law*. London: MIND.

Gostin L. (1983). *The Court of Protection*. London: MIND.

Gostin L. (1984). *Mental Health Services and the Law*, 5th edn. London: Shaw & Sons.

Gostin L. Contemporary historical approaches to mental health legislation. *J. Law and Society* (in press).

Gostin L., Rassaby E., Buchan A. *Mental Health Review Tribunals*. London: Oyez Longman (in press).

Hoggett B. *Social Work and Law: Mental Health*, 2nd edn. London: Sweet & Maxwell (in press).

Jones R. M., ed. (1982). *The Mental Health Act 1983: With Annotations*. London: Sweet & Maxwell.

Kinahan A. (1983). *Mental Health Act 1983: Current Law Statutes Reprints.* London: Sweet & Maxwell.

MIND (1981). *The Mental Health Year Book 1981/82.* London: MIND.

MIND (1983). *The Mental Health Case Law Review.* London: MIND.

Olsen R., Meacher M., Gostin L. (1983). *A Guide to the Mental Health Act.* Birmingham: BASW.

Olsen M. R. (1984). *Social Work and Mental Health.* London: Tavistock Publications.

Smith R., Rowland M. (1985). *Rights Guide to Non-Means Tested Benefits.* London: Child Poverty Action Group.

Szmukler G. I. (1981). Compulsory admission in a London borough. *Psychological Med.*; **11**: 825–38.

Taylor E. R. (1978). *Heywood and Massey: Court of Protection Practice.* London: Stevens & Sons.

Venables H. D. (1975). *A Guide to the Law Affecting Mental Patients.* Guildford: Butterworths.

Whitehead T. (1982). *Mental Illness and the Law.* Oxford: Blackwells.

Chapter 20

A Note on Forensic Psychiatry

It is the task of forensic psychiatry to diagnose and, where appropriate treat offenders who might be suffering from a mental illness. Where a conviction is made, and the offender is diagnosed as suffering from a mental illness, the court has a range of directions it can take: a probation order with a condition of psychiatric treatment attached (as an in-patient or out-patient); placement in an open mental hospital; placement in a secure unit; placement in special hospital; placement in prison.

The decision on placement will depend on several factors, the main ones being: the severity of the offence, the type of mental illness including in particular its treatability, and last but by no means least, the availability of suitable resources. When deciding on placement, the courts can take into account, or call for, social enquiry reports, and medical reports.

SOCIAL WORK ASPECTS

Clearly, either a probation officer or a social worker (and sometimes both together) could be involved in the social care of a mentally disordered offender. The needs generated by mental illness are the same, whether the sufferer has committed a criminal offence or not (see Chapters 1 and 5). The crucial additional factor is that the offence will give a person the status and stigma of being known as a criminal: and a mentally ill one, at that. This will manifest itself in their feelings about themselves, their position in the eyes of fellow patients ('he is under the forensic psychiatrist'), their position in society ('mad rapist', 'child stealer'), and sometimes, the secret fear or loathing in the eyes of professional helpers.

That is not to say that we must not learn from experience. For example, it may be important for workers to undertake joint visits to the homes of ex-patients who have a history of serious violent episodes (see Chapter 4). Stigma, however, is an inappropriate response and is an added burden for the mentally ill person to carry. Social work, whether undertaken by the social worker or probation officer cannot help but take account of this area. For example, the young female arsonist on discharge from hospital may well find community, non-institutional, placement hard to obtain in view of her history of arson. This will be so, even if her arson was generated by delusional ideas as a consequence of mental illness which has been treated and is now under control.

THE LEGAL FRAMEWORK

Part III of the Mental Health Act 1983 draws on proposals from the Butler Committee (1975) in terms of the assessment and treatment of offenders. It is comparatively rare for social workers to encounter clients subject to Part III proceedings, and thus we do not set out in detail the provisions of the Act. Readers are referred elsewhere for this. Here we endeavour to provide a guide to the main provisions in order to help social workers navigate a course through a difficult body of legislation.

It is important to note that in none of the criminal proceedings do social workers or probation officers have a statutory responsibility for admission, treatment or assessment. These are matters which are the jurisdiction of the courts, who in the main depend upon medical recommendations.

The Sections of the Act can be summarised as follows.

Section 35: remand to hospital for medical report

Duration: Up to 28 days, renewable for up to 12 weeks.
Includes: All categories of mental disorder.
Procedure: Remand by Court or Magistrate's Court on the evidence of a doctor.
Notes: No treatment without consent. Patient entitled to commission independent report at his own expense.

Section 36: remand for treatment

Duration: Up to 28 days at a time and not more than 12 weeks in all.
Includes: Mental illness and severe mental impairment.
Procedure: Remand by Crown Court on the evidence of two doctors.
Notes: Remand to hospital only where bail is not possible.

Section 37: hospital order

Duration: Six months, renewable for a further six months and then periods of one year at a time.

Includes: All categories of mental disorder, but in the case of psychopathic disorder or mental impairment may only be invoked where treatment is likely to alleviate or prevent a deterioration of the patient's condition.

Procedure: Order by Crown or Magistrate's Court on the medical evidence of two doctors.

Notes: Patient can apply to mental health review tribunal. Under Section 37, a court can also order *guardianship*.

Section 38: interim hospital order for assessment or hospital order

Duration: 12 weeks, renewable up to six months.

Procedure: Crown or Magistrate's Court.

Section 41: restriction order

Duration: No limit.

Includes: Where such an order is necessary for the protection of the public from serious harm.

Procedure: Crown Court, on the evidence of two doctors.

Notes: Only Home Secretary or mental health review tribunal can order discharge.

Other sections

Other sections of the Mental Health Act 1983 which social workers or probation officers may encounter are Sections 47, 48 and 49.

Sections 47 deals with the transfer to hospital of a person serving a sentence of imprisonment. It has the same effect as a hospital order (Section 37) and is invoked by the Home Secretary.

Section 48 deals with the transfer to hospital of prisoners who are not serving sentence of imprisonment (for example, people on remand, detainees under the Immigration Act).

Section 49 deals with the transfer of patients from prison to hospital with restrictions on discharge lasting to end of sentence.

OTHER LEGISLATION

Other legislation which comes into force with respect to offenders and persons on trial are the Criminal Procedure (Insanity) Act 1964, Sections 2 and 4 ('Special verdict of not guilty by reason of insanity' and 'Unfit to plead', respectively), Homicide Act 1957, Section 2 ('Diminished responsibility').

In addition, Section 3 of the Powers of Criminal Courts Act 1973 enables a court to make a probation order, for a period not exceeding three years, with a requirement that the offender submit to in-patient or out-patient psychiatric treatment provided that the patient consents, a hospital will accept him, and on the oral or written evidence of one doctor indicating that the offender's condition needs, and may be amenable to, treatment, but is not such so as to warrant detention under a hospital order.

Readers will appreciate that where any serious offences have been committed, or are suspected, close liaison with a solicitor or legal adviser is advisable as a matter of urgency.

REFERENCES AND FURTHER READING

Adler F. (1976). *Sisters in Crime*. Maidenhead: McGraw-Hill.

Confederation of Health Service Employees (1977). *The Management of Violent or Potentially Violent Patients*. London: COHSE.

Craft M., Craft A., eds. (1984). *Mentally Abnormal Offenders*. Eastbourne: Baillière Tindall.

Eysenck H. J. (1970). *Crime and Personality*. London: Granada.

Flew A. (1973). *Crime or Disease?* London: Macmillan.

Hamilton J. R., Freeman K. (1982). *Dangerousness: Psychiatric Assessment and Management*. London: Gaskell.

Klein M. (1981). On criminality (1934). In *Love, Guilt and Reparation and Other Works*, 1921–45. London: Hogarth Press and Institute of Psychoanalysis.

Prins H. (1980). *Offenders, Deviants or Patients*. London: Tavistock Publications.

Smart C. (1976). *Women, Crime, and Criminology*. London: Routledge & Kegan Paul.

Smith R. (1984). *Prison Health Care*. London: BMA.

Szasz T. (1974). *Law, Liberty and Psychiatry*. London: Routledge & Kegan Paul.

Walker N. (1978). Dangerous people. *Int. J. Law and Psychiatry*; **1**: 37–49.

Appendix

Resources for the Mentally Ill and/or their Relatives

Mind

National Association for Mental Health (MIND), 22 Harley Street, London
  WIN 2ED
Tel: 01–637 0741

MIND regional offices
Northern MIND, 158 Durham Road, Gateshead NE8 4EL
Tel: 091–478 4425

North West MIND, 21 Ribblesdale Place, Preston, Lancashire PR1 3NA
Tel: (0772) 21734/22790

Trent and Yorkshire MIND, First Floor Suite, White Buildings, Fitzallan
  Square, Sheffield S1 2AY
Tel: (0742) 21742

Wales MIND, 23 St Mary Street, Cardiff CF1 12AA
Tel: (0222) 395123

West Midlands MIND, Princess Chambers (3rd Floor), 52/54 Lichfield Street,
  Wolverhampton WV1 1DG
Tel: (0902) 24404

South West MIND, Blue Coat House, Sawclose, Bath BA1 1EY
Tel: (0225) 64670

Schizophrenia

National Schizophrenia Fellowship, 79 Victoria Road, Surbiton, Surrey KT6
  4NS
Tel: 01–390 3651

Northern Schizophrenia Fellowship, 38 Collingwood Buildings, Collingwood
  Street, Newcastle Upon Tyne NE1 1JH
Tel: (0632) 614343

North West Fellowship, 10/12 Beaumont Street, Warrington, Cheshire WA1 1UW
Tel: (0295) 571680

LINK/Glasgow Association for Mental Health, 2 Queen's Crescent, Glasgow GH4 9BL
Tel: 041-332 2541

Children and adolescents

NSPCC (HQ), 67 Saffron Hill, London EC1N 8RS
Tel: 01-242 1626

Association for Family Therapy, Department of Psychological Medicine, The Hospital for Sick Children, Gt Ormond Street, London WC1N 1EH
Tel: 01-831 0975

Invalid Children's Aid Association, 126 Buckingham Palace Road, London SW1 95B
(national)
Tel: 01-730 9891

National Association for Disabled Children, 1 South Audley Street, London W1Y 6TJ
Tel: 01-499 1188

National Association of Young People in Care, Salem House, 28a Manor Row, Bradford BD1 4QU
Tel: (0274) 728484/733134

National Autistic Society, 276 Willesden Lane, London NW2 5RB
Tel: 01-451 3844

North East Children's Society, 1a Claremont Street, Newcastle Upon Tyne NE2 4AH
Tel: (0632) 323741

Save the Children, 157 Clapham Road, London SW9
(national and international)
Tel: 01-582 1414

Thomas Coram Foundation for Children, 40 Brunswick Square, London WC1N 1AZ
Tel: 01-278 2424

Young Concern, 31 Cambridge Road, Hastings TN34 1DJ
Tel: (0424) 441708

National Association for the Welfare of Children in Hospital (NAWCH), Argyle House, 29-31 Euston Road, London NW1 2SD
Tel: 01-833 2041

Hyperactive Children's Support Group, Secretary: Sally Bunday, 59 Meadowside, Angmering, Littlehampton, West Sussex BN16 4BW (correspondence address)

Brook Advisory Centre for Young People, 233 Tottenham Court Road, London WIP 9AE
Tel: 01–580 2991

Elderly

Alzheimer's Disease Society, Bank Buildings, 3rd Floor, Fulham Broadway, London SW6
Tel: 01–381 4647

Age Concern England, Bernard Sunley House, 60 Pitcairn Road, Mitcham, Surrey CR4 3LL
Tel: 01–640 5431

Age Concern Scotland, 33 Castle Street, Edinburgh EH2 3DN
Tel: 031–225 5000

Age Concern Wales, 1 Park Grove, Cardiff, South Glamorgan CF1 3BJ
Tel: (0222) 371821

Age Concern Northern Ireland, 128 Great Victoria Street, Belfast BT2 7BG
Tel: (0232) 245729

Care and Counsel for the Elderly, 131 Middlesex Street, London E1 7JF (national)
Tel: 01–621 1624

Help the Aged, 32 Dover Street, London W1A 2AP (national)
Tel: 01–499 0972

National Confederation of Registered Rest Homes Association, 74 London Road, St Leonard's on Sea, East Sussex TN37 6AS
Tel: (0424) 712982

CRUSE (for widows and widowers) (Head Office), 126 Sheen Road, Richmond, Surrey TW9 1UR
Tel: 01–940 4818

Suicide

Samaritans: local branches listed in telephone directory.

Poisons Information Services:

New Cross Hospital, Avonly Road, London SE14 5ER
Tel: 01–407 7600

Royal Infirmary, 1 Launston Place, Edinburgh EH3 9YW
Tel: 031–229 2477

Royal Victoria Hospital, Grosvenor Road, Belfast B12 6BB
Tel: (0232) 40503

Jervis Street Hospital, Dublin
Tel: (0001) 745588

Ambulance Headquarters, Old Ty-Bronna, Fairwater Road, Fairwater, Cardiff
CF5 3XP
Tel: (0222) 569200

Problem drinkers

Accept (Alcoholism Community Centres for Education prevention and treatment), 200 Seagrave Road, London SW6 1RQ
Tel: 01–381 3155

Al-Anon Family Groups, 61 Great Dover Street, London SE1 4YF
Tel: 01–403 0888

Alcoholics Anonymous, PO Box 514, 11 Redcliffe Gardens, London SW10 9RG
Tel: 01–834 8202/352 9779

Aquarius Centre, 41 Newhall Street, Birmingham B3 3QD
Tel: 021–233 1268

Richmond Fellowship, Trelawn, 30 Russell Hill, Purley, Surrey CR2 2JA
Tel: 01–660 4586

Richmond Fellowship, Allen House, 112 Aldwick Road, Bognor Regis, Sussex
PO21 2PD
Tel: (0243) 827414

Local councils on alcoholism
Avon: 14 Park Row, Bristol BS1 5LJ
Tel: (0272) 293028/9

Birmingham: 32 Essex Street, Birmingham B5 4TR
Tel: 021–622 2041

Cumbria: 6 West Walls, Carlisle CA3 8UG
Tel: (0228) 44140

Doncaster: 28 Copley Road, Doncaster, South Yorkshire DN1 2PF
Tel: (0302) 68705

Hampshire: 18 West Park Road, Southampton SO1 0GA
Tel: (0703) 30219

North East: Mea House, Ellison Place, Newcastle Upon Tyne NE1 8XS
Tel: (0632) 320797

Sheffield: 629–631 Abbeydale Road, Sheffield S7 2BB
Tel: (0742) 587553

Somerset: 3 Upper High Street, Taunton, Somerset TA1 3PX
Tel: (0823) 88174

West Glamorgan: 75 Uplands Crescent, Swansea, West Glamorgan 5H0 0EY
Tel: (0792) 472519

Problem drug users

Residential
Phoenix House, 1 Eliot Bank, Forest Hill, London SE23 3XE
Tel: 01–699 5748

City Roads (Crisis Intervention) Ltd., 358 City Road, London EC1V 2PY
Tel: 01–278 8671

Turning Point, 8 Strutton Ground, London SW1P 2HP
Tel: 01–222 6862

Specialist advice and information service
Institute for the Study of Drug Dependence, 1–4 Hatton Place, Hatton Garden,
    London EC1N 8ND
Tel: 01–430 1991

Merseyside Drugs Council, 25 Hope Street, Liverpool L1 9BQ
Tel: 051–709 0074

Non-specialist advice and information services
Release, 1 Elgin Avenue, London W9 3PR
Tel: 01–603 8654

Lifeline Project Day Centre, Joddrell Street, Manchester M3 3HE
Tel: 061–832 6353

Others
TACADE (incorporating the Teachers' Advisory Council on Alcohol and Drug
    Education and the Health Education Unit), 2 Mount Street, Manchester M2
    5NG
Tel: 061–834 7210

Health Education Council Resource Centre, 75 New Oxford Street, London
    WC1A 1AH
Tel: 01–637 1881

Narcotics Anonymous
Tel: 01–351 6794

Mental impairment

Campaign for Mentally Handicapped, 16 Fitzroy Square, London W1P 5HQ
(national)
Tel: 01–387 9571

Elfrida Rathbone Society, 83 Mosley Street, Manchester M1 3GW
(national)
Tel: 061–236 5358

National Society for Mentally Handicapped Children, 123 Golden Lane,
London EC1Y 0RT
Tel: 01–253 9433

Scottish Society for the Mentally Handicapped, 13 Elmbank Street, Glasgow
G2 4QA
Tel: 041–226 4541

Downs Children's Association, 4 Oxford Street, London W1N 9FL
Tel: 01–580 0511

SPOD (Sexual and Personal Relationships and the Disabled), 286 Camden
Road, London N7 0BJ
Tel: 01–607 8851

Deaf people

Department of Psychiatry for the Deaf, Whittingham Hospital, Whittingham,
Nr Preston PR3 2JH
Tel: (0772) 865531

Regional Psychiatric Units for the Deaf, Springfield Hospital, 61 Glenburnie
Road, London SW17 7DJ
Tel: 01–672 9911

Certificate in Deaf Studies Course, Polytechnic of North London, Ladbroke
House, 60/62 Highbury Grove, London N5 2AD
(CCETSW Approved Post Qualifying Training Course)
Tel: 01–607 2789

Certificate in Social Work with the Deaf Course, Moray House, College of
Education, Holyrood Road, Edinburgh EH8 8AQ
Tel: 031–556 8455

Gartnavel Royal Hospital, 1055 Great Western Road, Glasgow G12 0XH
Tel: 041–334 6241

Leverndale Hospital, 510 Crookston Road, Glasgow G53 7TN
Tel: 041–882 6255

Ethnic minorities

Joint Council for the Welfare of Immigrants, 115 Old Street, London EC1V 9JR
Tel: 01–251 8706

Commission for Racial Equality, Elliott House, Allington Street, London SW1E 5EH
Tel: 01–828 7022

Jewish Welfare Board (HQ), 221 Golders Green Road, London NW11 9DW
Tel: 01–458 3282

West Indian Concern, Caribbean House, Shoreditch Park, Bridport Place, London N1 5DS
Tel: 01–729 0986

Psychotherapy

Resources through the UK are limited but constantly growing in number. Information on local psychotherapy facilities can be obtained from the responsible Area Health Authority. Some of the main centres in London are:

British Association of Psychotherapists, 121 Hendon Lane, London N3 3PR
Tel: 01–346 1747

The Institute of Psycho Analysis, New Cavendish Street, London W1N 7RD
Tel: 01–580 4952

The London Centre for Psychotherapy, 19 Fitzjohns Avenue, London NW3 5JY
Tel: 01–435 0873

The Society of Analytical Psychology, 1 Daleham Gardens, London NW3 5BY
Tel: 01–435 7696

The Tavistock Clinic, Belsize Lane, London NW3 5BA
Tel: 01–435 7111

Association for Group and Individual Psychotherapy, 29 St Mark's Crescent, London NW1 7TU
Tel: 01–485 9141

Women's Therapy Centre, 6 Manor Gardens, London N7 6LA
Tel: 01–263 6200

Marital and family therapy

Church of England Children's Society (HQ), Old Town Hall, Kennington Road, London SE11 4QD

(national network of family centres)
Tel: 01–735 2441

Family Welfare Association (HQ), 501 Kingsland Road, London E8 4AU
(national organisation, offering a variety of services for families)
Tel: 01–254 6257

Family Service Units (HQ), 207 Old Marylebone Road, London NW1 5QP
(national organisation with small, local offices offering intensive social work
   intervention)
Tel: 01–402 5175

National Marriage Guidance Council
(local branches in telephone directory)

National Council for One-Parent Families, 255 Kentish Town Road, London
   NW5 2LX
Tel: 01–267 1361

The Tavistock Clinic and Institute of Human Relations, 120 Belsize Lane,
   London NW3 5BA
(intensive marital, family and child therapy, mainly for London area)
Tel: 01–435 7111

Counselling and self-help

Westminster Pastoral Foundation, 23 Kensington Square, London W8 5MN
(national)
Tel: 01–937 6956

The Phobics Society, 4 Cheltenham Road, Chorlton-cum-Hardy, Manchester
   M21 1QN
(national)
Tel: 061–881 1937

Gay Switchboard
(London)
Tel: 01–837 7324 (24 hr, every day)

Psychiatric Rehabilitation Association, 21a Kingsland High Road, London E8
   2JS
(London)
Tel: 01–254 9753

Rape Crisis Centre, PO Box 69, London WC1X 9NJ
(London)
Tel: 01–837 1600 (24 hr telephone service; also for information on nationwide
   resources)

Gamblers' Anonymous, 17/23 Blantyre Street, Cheyne Walk, London SW10
   0DT

(national)
Tel: 01–352 3060

Ex-Servicemen's Mental Welfare Society, Secretary: Capt. J. S. LeBlanc Smith
  RN, 37 Thurloe Street, London SW7 2LL
(national)
Tel: 01–584 8688

British Epilepsy Association:

Bigshotte, New Wokingham Road, Wokingham, Berkshire
Tel: 034–463 122

313 Chapeltown Road, Leeds
Tel: (0532) 621076

Guildhall Buildings, Navigation Street, Birmingham
Tel: 021–643 7524

Room 16, Claremont Street Hospital, Belfast
Tel: (0232) 248214

National Information Centre for Anorexic Family Aid, Sackville Place, 44/48
  Magdalen Street, Norwich NR3 1JE
Tel: (0604) 21414

Good Practices in Mental Health, 380 Harrow Road, London W9 2HU
Tel: 01–289 2034

Accommodation

The Mental After Care Association, Eagle House, 110 Jermyn Street, London
  SW1Y 6HB
(national, for adult mentally ill)
Tel: 01–839 5953

Richmond Fellowship, 8 Addison Road, London W14 8DL
(national and international, for adult and adolescent mentally ill)
Tel: 01–603 6373

Leonard Cheshire Foundation, Leonard Cheshire House, 26–29 Maunsel
  Street, London SW1P 2QN
(national, for physically and mentally handicapped people, including those with
  history of mental illness)
Tel: 01–828 1822

Salvation Army, Social Services HQ, 280 Mare Street, London E8 1HE
(national, all client groups considered)
Tel: 01–985 1181

National Association of Voluntary Hostels, 33 Long Acre, London WC2E 9LA

(advice and placement service *only*. All client groups, but referral must be made through professional agency)
Tel: 01–240 0665

Association of Therapeutic Communities, St Luke's Centre, 3 Greaves Tower, World's End Estate, London SW10 0EA
(advice and coordination *only*, on all aspects of the therapeutic community movement)
Tel: 01–352 7026

Multi-disciplinary team: professional associations

Royal College of Psychiatrists, 17 Belgrave Square, London SW1X 8PG
Tel: 01–235 2351

Royal College of Nursing, Cavendish Square, London W1M 0AB
Tel: 01–409 3333

British Association of Social Workers, 16 Kent Street, Birmingham B5 6RD
Tel: 021–622 3911

British Psychological Society, St Andrew's House, 48 Princess Road East, Leicester LE1 7DR
Tel: (0533) 549568

British Association of Occupational Therapists, 20 Rede Place, Off Chepstow Place, London W2 4TU
Tel: 01–229 9738

British Institute of Industrial Therapy, 99 Leigh Road, Eastleigh, Hampshire SO5 4DR
Tel: (0703) 642988

British Association for Counselling, 37a Sheep Street, Rugby CV2 13BX
Tel: (0788) 78328/9

Volunteers

The Volunteer Centre, 29 Lower Kings Road, Berkhamsted, Hertfordshire HP4 2AB
(national)
Tel: (044 27) 73311

National Council for Voluntary Organisations, 26 Bedford Square, London WC1B 3HU
(national)
Tel: 01–636 4066

Community Service Volunteers, 237 Pentonville Road, London N1 9NJ
(national)
Tel: 01–278 6601

Rights groups

MIND (National Association for Mental Health), 22 Harley Street, London
  WIN 2ED
Tel: 01–637 0741

Release, c/o 1 Elgin Avenue, London W9 3PR
Tel: 01–603 8654 (24 hr)

Child Poverty Action Group (CPAG), 1 Macklin Street, London WC2B 5NH
Tel: 01–242 9149

National Council for Civil Liberties, 21 Tabard Street, London SE1 4LA
Tel: 01–403 3888

Citizens Advice Bureau
(local branches listed in telephone directory)

The Children's Legal Centre, 20 Compton Terrace, London N1 2UN
Tel: 01–359 6251

The Patients' Association, 11 Dartmouth Street, London SW1H 9BN
Tel: 01–222 4992

Forensic psychiatry: services for offenders

Prisoners' Wives and Families Society, 254 Caledonian Road, Islington,
  London N1 0NG
(national)
Tel: 01–278 3981

Rainer Foundation, 89a Blackheath Hill, London SE10 8TJ
(national)
Tel: 01–691 3654

Resettlement of Offenders Coordinating Committee, Lee House, St Thomas
  Street, Winchester SO23 9HJ
(Hampshire)
Tel: (0962) 61323

Constellation (Lancashire Probation and After-Care Service Coordinating
  Group): Stephen House, 1st Floor, Bethesda Street, Burnley, Lancashire S1
  2PQ
Tel: (0742) 26477 extn. 289

National Association for the Care and Resettlement of Offenders (NACRO),
  169 Clapham Road, London SW9 0PU
Tel: 01–592 6500

NACRO regional offices
Bath: 4 Cheap Street, Bath, BA1 1NE
Tel: (0225) 62581

Manchester: 567a Barlow Moor Road, Manchester M21 2AE
Tel: 061–861 9737

Scotland: SACRO, 110 West Bow, Grassmarket, Edinburgh EH1 2HH
Tel: 031–225 5232

Northern Ireland: NIACRO, 41 Donegall Street, Belfast BT1 2PG
Tel: (0232) 20157

Legal issues

Mental health act commission offices

Liverpool: Cressington House, 249 St Mary's Road, Garston, Liverpool L19
0NF
Tel: 051–427 2061

London: Floors 1 and 2, Hepburn House, Marsham Street, London SW1P
4HW
Tel: 01–211 8061

Nottingham: Spur A, Block 5, Government Buildings, Chalfont Drive,
Western Boulevard, Nottingham NG8 3RZ
Tel: (0602) 293409

Clerk to the Tribunal, Mental Health Review Tribunals, 15th Floor, Euston
Tower, 286 Euston Road, London NW1 3DN
(special hospital in region: Broadmoor Hospital)
Tel: 01–388 1188 extn. 787

Clerk to the Tribunal, Mental Health Review Tribunals, 3rd Floor, Cressington House, 249 St Mary's Road, Garston, Liverpool L19 0NF
(special hospitals in region: Moss Side Hospital and Park Lane Hospital)
Tel: 051–469 0095

Clerk to the Tribunal, Mental Health Review Tribunals, Spur A, Block 5,
Government Buildings, Chalfont Drive, Western Boulevard, Nottingham
NG8 3RZ
(special hospital in region: Rampton Hospital)
Tel: (0602) 294222/3

Clerk to the Tribunal, Mental Health Review Tribunals, 2nd Floor, New
Crown Buildings, Cathays Park, Cardiff CF1 3NQ
Tel: (0222) 825798

Legal aid offices

Birmingham: Podium Centre City House (Smallbrook Queensway), 5 Hill
Street, Birmingham B5 4UD
Tel: 021–632 6541

Brighton: 9–12 Middle Street, Brighton BN1 1AS
Tel: (0273) 27003

Bristol: Whitefriars, Block C, Lewins Mead, Bristol BS1 2LR
Tel: (0272) 214801

Cambridge: Kett House, Station Road, Cambridge CB1 2RF
Tel: (0223) 66511

Cardiff: Marland House, Central Square, Cardiff CF1 1PF
Tel: (0222) 388971

Chester: Pepper House, Pepper Square, Chester CH1 1DF
Tel: (0244) 315455

Leeds: City House, New Station Street, Leeds LS1 4JS
Tel: (0532) 442851

Liverpool: Moor House, James Street, Liverpool L2 7SA
Tel: 051–236 8371

London: 29–37 Red Lion Street, London WC1R 4PP
Tel: 01–405 6991

Manchester: Pall Mall Court, 67 King Street, Manchester M60 9AX
Tel: 061–832 7112

Newcastle Upon Tyne: Eagle Star House, Fenkle Street, Newcastle Upon Tyne
   NE1 5RU
Tel: (0632) 323461

Nottingham: 5 Friar Lane, Nottingham NG1 6BW
Tel: (0602) 412424

Reading: 80 Kings Road, Reading RG1 4LT
Tel: (0734) 589696

A list of solicitors who specialise in undertaking mental health review tribunal
representation is available from:

The Law Society, 113 Chancery Lane, London WC2
Tel: 01–242 1222

Index